by *Pierre Daninos*

THE SECRET OF MAJOR THOMPSON

1957

THE NOTEBOOKS OF MAJOR THOMPSON

1955

These are BORZOI BOOKS

published in New York by ALFRED A. KNOPF

The Secret of

MAJOR THOMPSON

by Pierre Daninos

TRANSLATED FROM THE FRENCH BY

W. MARMADUKE THOMPSON
C.S.I., D.S.O., O.B.E.

Illustrated by Walter Goetz

The Secret of

MAJOR
THOMPSON

1957

ALFRED · A · KNOPF

NEW YORK

TRANSLATED BY DON CORTES

L. C. catalog card number: 57–12575

© *Alfred A. Knopf, Inc., 1957*

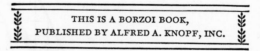

THIS IS A BORZOI BOOK,
PUBLISHED BY ALFRED A. KNOPF, INC.

FIRST AMERICAN EDITION

ORIGINALLY PUBLISHED *in France as* Le Secret du Major Thompson. *Copyright by Librairie Hachette 1956. Published in Great Britain by Jonathan Cape, Ltd. under the title of* Major Thompson and I.

Contents

The Secret of

MAJOR THOMPSON

Translator's Preface

"BUT, MAJOR, THAT ISN'T FRANCE AT ALL!"

Some of our readers may be wondering how on earth I came to help my good friend Pierre Daninos write a book about Anglo-Saxons—a race of mortals whom, I need hardly add, no Frenchman can ever really understand. Well, it all began one day when I was walking past the French National Assembly with Pochet. Pointing my umbrella up at the pillared façade, I said to him:

"Well, and what do you think of your Chamber?"

"*My* Chamber? First of all, *mon cher Major,* you know perfectly well it isn't '*my* Chamber.'"

"But it is the Chamber of all the French people . . . and didn't you vote for it?"

"Tss, tss, but of course. But, come, come, Major, that's not France at all!"

For Pochet—and the same goes for Taupin—France is never *that* at all. France isn't three million Socialists. It isn't two million Radicals, nor three million Independent Peasants. Nor, obviously, is it five million Communists. And, good lord! who would dream of suggesting that it might be fifty-two Poujadiste deputies? As for that Parisian couple I bumped into last election day on the ski-slopes in Switzerland who made it quite clear they were casting blank ballots, how could I ever have thought that that was *la France?* Only a subversive wretch could entertain such a notion. Just as only a damned fool could confuse France with those young conscripts who recently held up the train on their way from the barracks. As Colonel Turlot said to me: "A handful of hotheads who've gotten out of step and whom we'll soon get back into line! But France, the real France, isn't that at all!"

It was the same story the day those strikers at Orly forced me to get off the plane as it was about to take off for London, and to stumble about in the dead of night, just because they hadn't gotten their strike pay. Here again I was given to understand by Pochet that this was all the work of a handful of agitators and disturbers of the peace

who were quite obviously unrepresentative. *Voyons, donc,*
that wasn't France at all!

"France, Major, is a country that works! Take a trip up
north and you'll have something to write home about!"
said my friend, without realizing that this was precisely
the direction of my intended journey. "You'll see. They're
at their desks when you're still in bed!"

Pochet was so persuasive that it was I who suffered
from a guilt complex when they were ejecting me from the
airport. I must say that Pochet seemed a trifle upset by
the whole business. On our way back to Paris in his car
he went through a red light. A *gendarme* stopped him and
gave him the devil. Pochet kept unusually quiet, but once
we were on our way again, he smiled.

"Too bad about that summons, isn't it?" I said to him.

He made a deprecating gesture. "I'll get it fixed. I have
a friend at the Prefecture of Police!"

I asked him if this was standard French practice.

"Fortunately not. It would all be too easy otherwise!
You've got to know somebody, *voilà!*"

I was suddenly reminded of some French motorists I
had helped out last summer by turning around and going
back ten kilometers to fetch them a mechanic. Curious
thing—they insisted on inviting me to have dinner with

them the next time I passed through their town. *"Mais si, Monsieur,* we insist, it's so rare to find people on the road who are so considerate, and a foreigner at that . . . all the more reason!" But when I did come back and telephone them, they told me themselves that they weren't at home.

Yes, you have to be blissfully naïve—as only a naïve Englishman like me can be—to make generalizations about the French, particularly after you've had a Paris bus conductor say to you (as happened one day when I couldn't produce the proper fare):

"If you haven't any change on you, why don't you stay at home?" After which he grumbled his way through the bus muttering: *"Encore un Amerloque!"*[1]

Only a simpleton would think that France is that and overlook its people's characteristic courtesy. Still, it was my distinct impression that the bus was full of Frenchmen, for shortly after the conductor's outburst we got caught in a traffic jam and I heard someone exclaim:

"The first thing I'd do would be to get those fat foreign cars off the road so as to make room for people to move!"

But I was doubtless mistaken and, in fact, it must

[1] French slang for "Another ruddy American!"

have been a Yemenite bus that I boarded at the Porte Saint-Martin. For when I told Pochet about it, he said:

"*Soyons sérieux, Major!* France, after all, isn't a bus! You may have had a run-in with an ill-humored bus conductor, but you know as well as I do that France doesn't conduct herself that way!"

"It's amazing, all right, how wrong one can be about France! Not long ago, for example, when Taupin was taking me to call on one of his friends, he warned me before we got there:

"Call him *Monsieur le Président*. It will please him no end."

"Of course," I said, "but *Président* of what?"

"Well," said Taupin, "he's the *Vice Président* of the Limoges chapter of the Skins and Hides Guild."

"In that case, shouldn't I call him *Monsieur le Vice Président?*"

"Anything but that!" cried Taupin. "It's like calling someone 'Lieutenant Colonel.'"

I remember that I had that very same day met the President of the Virgin Cinematographic Film Guild and the President of the Linoleum Orphanage, and I began to wonder if every Frenchman weren't the President of something.

7

"Mais non," Taupin told me. "I am, as it happens, the President of Les Amis de la Pédale Gasco-Béarnaise.[2] But that doesn't mean that all Frenchmen are like that."

Can it be that the French are never "like that"?

When—to cite another example—I walk into the waiting-room of that good dentist, or perhaps I should say stomatologist, Dr. Dusseloup, and find only one weekly there that I can get my teeth into—a copy of the *Petit Explorateur Français,* reporting the activities of the Botanical Garden of Tananarive in the year 1898—the doctor explains to me:

"Que voulez-vous, Major? I can only keep the old ones; the rest get swiped."

When I complain to the manageress of the Hôtel des Flots Bleus because there's only one coat-hanger in my bedroom wardrobe (stolen, at that, by some transient from the Schweizerhof in Lucerne), she says to me: "They're always making off with them."

Or when I suggest to the *patron* of the Petit-Gastronome that he might at least put a box of paper towels in his toilets, he has a ready-made answer: "They wouldn't stay there one hour!"

~~~~~~~~~~~~~~~~~~~~~

[2] Literally "The Friends of the Gascon-Béarnais Pedal"—one of France's innumerable provincial cycling clubs.

All this makes me think that a foreigner who limited his tour of France to visiting a dentist, a restaurant, and a hotel might easily come away with the idea that the French are a nation of kleptomaniacs wary of pickpockets.

But it was useless trying to explain all this to Pochet.

"Frankly, Major, you exaggerate," he protested. "The French are not burglars."

As I wished at that very moment to shake out my pipe, Pochet handed me an ashtray inscribed: "Excelsior Palace Hotel, Roma."

"Souvenir of a trip," he offered, by way of explanation.

But I thought I saw him blush.

All the same, as I keep telling myself, how wrong one can be about the French! Take, for example, the time I was waiting in a rather dark and heavily scented corner for a young lady to finish her call in a telephone booth (which, I must say, was covered with the most shocking inscriptions). Every now and then the door would open slightly and I would hear her say: "*Allez, je te laisse. Y a un type qui attend, j'voudrais qu' tu voies sa bille! . . . Alors on se voit ce soir? . . . Allez, au revoir!*" [3] Each

wwwwwwwwwwww

[3] Colloquial French (not that of the Academy) which might be roughly translated: "All right, I must be off. There's a chap waiting, wish you could see the mug on 'im! . . . We'll see each other tonight? . . . All right, good-by!"

9

time I thought she had finished, the door would close and the conversation would go on. Do the French spend their time ringing each other up to say that they'll see each other and seeing each other to say that they'll ring up?

"But no," Pochet protested when I told him about this. "It was a woman, Major! *Ah, les femmes!* . . . France, after all, isn't that!"

Good heavens, then! What on earth is France?

When I finally put the question to Pochet and Taupin, neither of them took very kindly to it. Both treated my mild prodding as a kind of personal affront. Pochet remarked rather heatedly that my back-handed questioning —an *"interrogation sournoise"* he called it—was a typical example of "Anglo-Saxon hyprocrisy." As for Taupin, he attributed my "outburst" to passing ill-humor brought on by a row I had just had with my wife, Martine, over those long woollies I insist on wearing.[4] He followed this up by

〰〰〰〰〰〰〰〰

[4] Let me explain, at the risk of adding a footnote to my own preface, just what all the fuss was about. It was all a lamentable consequence of my being held up that night by those ruddy strikers at Orly, with the result that I caught a wopping cold and had to take refuge inside a pair of those heavy woollies which permit quinquagenarians like myself to brave the elements in mid-January without an overcoat. Besides, it's a gross overstatement to say I had a "row" with Martine. At most there took place an *échange de mots,* as the French so aptly put it. I put in a word with Martine and she exchanges it for half a dozen of her own, and at a much faster clip. I'm rather used to it now. But what I can't

"All right, I must be off. There's a chap waiting, wish you could see the mug on 'im!"

accusing me of being out of sorts because Martine and I couldn't agree on the proper schooling to be given our second son, Nicholas.

But to get back to the point of this foreword. Having failed to make much headway with Pochet and Taupin, I thought I would turn to my old friend Daninos and see if he could do any better enlightening me as to what France, the real France, really is. He listened to me, I'm afraid, with growing impatience and finally hit the roof.

"Major!" he protested, "I've had enough of your sarcastic jibes at the French! For two whole years I've put up with your *British rule.* I offered you my help in translating your Notebooks into French and all I got out of it was your grudging permission to slip in an occasional footnote in which I could speak up for my compatriots. But now I've had enough! Put down your pen and, since you're on the warpath, take up your rifle—"

"Express Magnum .375 . . ."

"All right, take the express if you want and go back to India. But with your permission I'm going to do a little

wwwwwwwwwwwwww

get used to is the tone of command she adopts with regard to things as personal and private as my underdrawers. "Do take off that frightful long underwear, Marminet, I entreat you, and put on your overcoat!" I ask you: is this the sort of disrespect a former officer in the Indian army should put up with? Definitely not.

traveling of my own. In fact, Major, I've a mind to visit England . . . and perhaps I might even go on and visit your distant cousins in America . . . so that I can report in my turn just what you are or are not like!"

"Now, don't get excited, Daninos," I said. "Where is your self-control? As a matter of fact, your idea isn't such a bad one. But—"

"But what?"

"Well," I said, trying to put it as tactfully as possible, "you really don't mean to say you're going to write a book all by yourself?"

"It's something I've done already."

"Yes, old boy, but it wasn't a book about Anglo-Saxons."

"All right, Major, I'll get Pochet to help me . . . and Sonia, too, for that matter."

Great Scott! I thought.

"And what about me?" I remonstrated. "By Jove, you really can't object to my tagging along with you on your visit to the British Isles, just as you accompanied me on my sentimental journey through France. Yes, and it wouldn't be such a bad idea either to let me put a word in now and again whenever you find yourself getting a little out of your depth . . ."

"All right, Major, have it your own way. But I shall

1 3

be less tight-fisted than you. I'll gladly yield you the pen
. . . and not just for the footnotes, but, on occasion, if you
feel like it, for whole pages at a time."

"It's a bargain!" I said. "You go on over to London
ahead of me. In a couple of weeks my dear wife and I
shall be at our place in Hampshire—it's always easier and
quieter to be at home to talk over Nicholas's schooling.
So we'll meet over there. But as you're going over first, I
suggest that after spending a night or two in a hotel you
move over to my old friend Mrs. Cripplestone's. Her
boardinghouse will give you a splendid opportunity for
sampling a bit of healthy British life. So, cheerio, old man
. . . and good luck!"

And that's how it all started.

Chapter 1

[P.D.]

"BUT ENGLAND, MAJOR, ISN'T THAT EITHER!"

Ten minutes on the soil of Albion were enough to make me realize that England was not at all what Major Thompson claimed.

As I boarded the London boat train at Dover, I sought to keep in mind the essential rules of British conduct which the Major had carefully instilled in me:

1. The English never speak to someone unless they have been properly introduced (except in case of shipwreck).

2. You should never talk about God or your stomach.

But at lunch the very first Englishman I found seated opposite me, instead of saying "No, thank you" like a

Frenchman, when I handed him the pickles, exclaimed:

"By God! How I'd love one of those pickles . . . but I've got a blasted stomach ulcer!"

I felt the Major's world reel and the very foundations of the Empire rock under my feet. I could almost hear the Major's voice expostulating:

"But, of course, that was a very poor breed of Englishman. England, Daninos, isn't that at all!"

Now, I'm certainly not going to claim right off the bat that all Englishmen take God's name in vain and talk to strangers about their stomachs, but . . . if France seemed to the Major a country of 43 million exceptions, I can safely say of Great Britain that it is an island made up of 53 million islets, for I have never met an Englishman who did not speak of his countrymen as though he himself were quite unlike them.

Actually, one of the hardest things, when you get to London, is to meet an Englishman. It's even harder in English history, in the making of which so many peoples have had a hand. There are times when you have to wait 600 years before running across a king who wasn't born in Osnabrück, Hannover, or Blois. The Canutes were Danes, the Plantagenets French, the Tudors Welsh, the Stuarts Scottish, and finally, after booting out a Scotsman to make way for a Dutchman, the English treated themselves to a German king who couldn't speak a word of English.[1]

Without going all the way back to drag in William the Conqueror, the first cab-driver who took me around London kept up an incessant tirade against the English in a curiously foreign accent. At every stop light he grumbled and spouted bits of the *Daily Worker*.[2] As we were driving by Buckingham Palace, he said to me over his shoulder:

"Ever thought of the number of cabbies they could put up in there?"

I said: "No." I had never considered Buckingham Palace from that angle. Surprised by such irreverence, I asked him why, as an Englishman, he didn't feel more attached to the Crown.

"I'm British, not English," he said. "I'm a Welshman."

I thought I might have better luck finding a really authentic Englishman at the hotel, but the manager proved to be Swiss, the desk clerk Belgian, the elevator man Malayan, the chambermaids Irish, the maître d'hôtel (and, of course, the chef) French, and the waiters Italian.

~~~~~~~~~~~~~~~~~~

[1] For God's sake! What does all this prove? A Turk can perfectly well be King of England. If we install him in Buckingham Palace, it's because he suits us, that's all. We don't ask him for his identity card (which, I might add, didn't exist before this last ruddy war). (W.M.T.)

[2] English Bolshevik rag. (W.M.T.)

The evening of my second day, having still not encountered an Englishman, I decided to take the matter up with the manager, Mr. Wenger Stücki: "I take it the owner is English?" I said.

"No, Monsieur. Mr. MacNamara, the owner of the chain of Elizabethan Hotels, is Scottish."

It's a serious mistake to think that England has never been occupied since 1066. She still is—by the Scots. They crossed the border of the Union in 1707 and have never gone back again. The Scots are a people who never feel really at home except at somebody else's—particularly when that somebody else is English. I learned from Mr. Wenger Stücki that 72.5 per cent of the key posts in the British hotel business, as in the ministries, the Coal Board, the textile firms, and the railways, were in Scottish hands. The English themselves enjoy telling the story about the Scotsman who, on his return to Edinburgh from London, was asked: "Well, so you saw our English friends?" and replied: "Hadn't a chance. I saw only the top men."

The only place in Great Britain where you almost never meet a Scotsman is in London's Soho. There you can spend a whole day without hearing anything but Italian, French, Spanish, Chinese, German, or Javanese, and you can see people lounging on their doorsteps, like vulgar continentals.

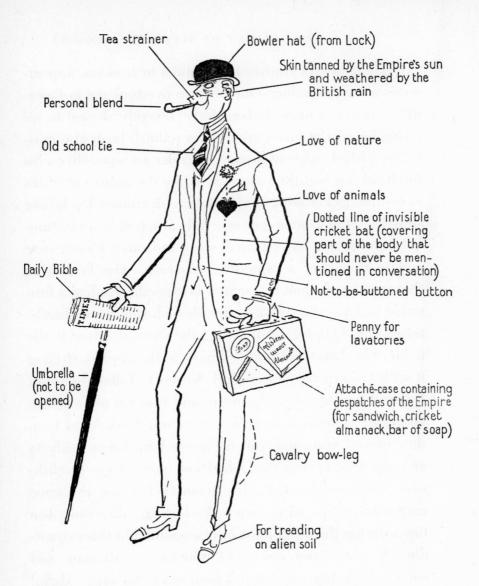

X-ray photograph of W.M.T., British Citizen.

There are, of course, Englishmen in London, appearances notwithstanding. One of them overtook me in Piccadilly. He was a man of about forty, severely elegant in his attire, his scarlet face crossed by a reddish bush of a mustache, a black, narrow-brimmed bowler set squarely on his forehead, his waistline emphasized by the smart cut of his navy-blue jacket with its side vents, his trouser leg falling straight to the gleaming shoe, a red carnation in his buttonhole, and in one hand a small weather-beaten leather case and in the other a rapier-like umbrella. The first thing that struck me about this man was his walk. He had a firm stride and a springy gait, and with each step his umbrella, raised chin-high by a deft flick of the wrist, revolved in the palm of his hand and then fell back to the ground, striking it with a sharp rap. Fascinated, I tried to follow him, but I almost had to run to keep up, and running after a man you don't know is one of the things you don't do in London, even if you think you recognize him. I was ready to give up, feeling sure that I had lost track of my Englishman, when suddenly, in the Haymarket, I saw the same man coming toward me from the opposite direction. Ten times during the day I must have encountered this extraordinarily ubiquitous and striking-looking gentleman, and each time I hurried toward him, ready to cry: "Hello! Major!"

But no! It wasn't Major Thompson. It was one of his countless brothers. London is a city where hundreds of thousands of bowlers, all planted on the same heads, advance to the conquest of the same invisible goals. Nowhere else in the world are there men who march toward their destiny as impassive and secure in their own rights as do the Londoners.

And just what is this destiny? For a long time I asked myself this question. Just what secrets of state, just what *most-secret dispatches* do these long-legged Edens carry about with them in their attaché cases?

One day I decided to follow one of them to the bitter end. Emerging from the Foreign Office, the black bowler turned into Whitehall, walked up the Mall, and then disappeared into the "tube" at St. James's Park. Thanks to some recent training, I managed to keep up with him. As soon as he sat down, he started to read *The Times*, but as we got farther from the center of the city and he found he had a whole seat to himself, he folded away his paper, placed his precious bag on his knees, and cautiously opened it. At last I was to be let into the secret of a Foreign Office attaché case!

The dispatches of the Empire on this particular day consisted of a bar of soap, a small white napkin, the *Cricket Almanac*, recognizable by its cover, and a ham sandwich, which the gentleman consumed, just as though he were traveling from Angoulême to Poitiers. I must admit he ate it very daintily. But the fact remains he ate.

A little later I told the Major of my discovery.

"Don't tell me, you confounded Frenchman," he cried, "that you're now persuaded that Foreign Office dispatch cases carry nothing in them but *casse-croûte,* to use your own rather vulgar expression!" [3]

Well, no. . . . But still, nothing so resembles one Englishman in a bowler hat as another Englishman in a bowler hat.[4] The philosopher J. R. Lowell himself once said:

wwwwwwwwwwwwww

[3] *Casse-croûte* is a French term literally meaning "break-crust," much as we say "break-fast." It is used to designate the traditional chunk of bread, accompanied by cheese or ham and often by the classic bottle of wine, which the French workingman (or woman) carries to work. (W.M.T.)

[4] For the benefit of the Major and those of my readers who think I've made all this up, I might add that several weeks later, when I told some English friends of this incident, they pulled out a copy of the *Woman's Own* Magazine (November 25, 1954) and showed me a letter in the Correspondence Column which ran: "The other day in the street I found an elegant gentleman in a bowler hat, striped trousers, and a black waistcoat walking alongside of me carrying an umbrella and an attaché case. All of a sudden his case struck a lamppost and out spilled the contents—two heads of lettuce!" (Letter from Miss L. Atkinson, Onchan, Isle of Man.) Think of it! The same attaché-case episode twice in one year! There must be some truth here after all. . . .

*A perplexed Pochet had arranged to meet the Major in
Piccadilly.*

"Never am I more grateful to Providence than when it has me meet an Englishman who is unlike the rest."

Whence springs this similarity?

The English can be explained by their Anglo-Saxon heritage and the influence of the Methodists. But I prefer to explain them in terms of tea, roast beef, and rain. A people is first of all what it eats, drinks, and gets pelted with. Men who are ceaselessly battered by the wind and the rain and shrouded in a permanent fog end up themselves turning into raincoats which shed criticism as easily as an oilskin sheds water. Men who drink tea seven times a day and eat the same vegetables and meats all year round naturally end up with the same rosy complexions. There is roast beef in the Englishman just as there is rice in the Chinaman.[5]

Indeed, how can one understand such people? How

[5] For once I find myself agreeing. If Frenchmen differ so much from one another, it's because one likes to sample his snails, while another savors his meat *pâté*, and the wife of the third brews him his pet stew—his *petit pot-au-feu à lui*—which is quite unlike the neighbor's. I'm never as rosy-hued as I am in France around three p.m., and, goodness knows, the Union Jack which you claim to find all over my face is tinted differently by Nuits-Saint-Georges than by the wine of Saumur. Your French Côtes-du-Rhône, your Clos-Vougeots, and your Muscadets give the French an infinite variety of coloration. Tea and Scotch condemn the British to greater uniformity. But aside from that, you simply can't understand us. (W.M.T.)

can you define people who make a point of never asking
personal questions about their neighbors' private lives,
but follow all the comings and goings and new acquisitions
of their Queen as though they were the *concierges* of
Buckingham Palace; who are stout champions of individual liberty, but close their pubs at three p.m. sharp;
who don't like to talk, but adore orators; who hate heat,
but love a good fire;[6] who have an innate sense of gran-
deur, but who—from their cottages and ponies to their
railway engines—carefully cultivate the small; who talk
of trifles when sober and begin to talk of serious things
when drinking; who do things like no one else in the world
and yet are astonished that the rest of the world doesn't
do the same; who consider *The Times* the most serious
newspaper in the world, but reserve its front page for
personal messages from gentlemen seeking traveling com-
panions; who see their children caned by their masters
without batting an eyelash, but cannot stand the sight of
a crippled sparrow; who are suspicious of everything that
isn't British, but who derive their national beverage from
a Chinese-Indian shrub; who wouldn't dream of kissing
in public in the subway or on the street, but who do it at

---

[*] There is perhaps no more delicate pleasure for an Englishman
than to sit in a lively draft in an Elizabethan or Tudor drawing-room
freezing his spine while he roasts his face in the hearth.

Hyde Park or Maidenhead before a public that's twice as large; who abhor cross-breeding, but are themselves an extraordinary cross-mixture of Celts, Saxons, Scandinavians, and Normans; who reproach the French for living to eat, but spend their time nibbling odds and ends; who dress informally in their castles, but insist on donning gray bowler hats and carnations before going to feel the udder of a Yorkshire cow at an Olympia exhibition; who remain the cradle of the most unbending conservatism, but who served as the incubator for Karl Marx and Lenin; who enforce austerity on the Sabbath while distributing a Sunday scandal weekly to eight million readers; who manufacture *bidets* for the rest of the world, but won't have one in the house,[7] who like to drive slowly while living, but get driven at breakneck speed in their Rollses when dead; who carry an umbrella when the sun is out and a raincoat when it pours; who are always chanting "Home, Sweet Home," but love to settle down abroad; who wouldn't for the world speak of the stomach, but who advertise contraceptives in their "chemist" shops; who are

[7] From Bruges to Zanzibar you can find bathrooms equipped with an impressive array of *bidets* labeled "Shanks and Co. Ltd., Barrhead, Scotland." But in Barrhead, Scotland, you will look for one in vain. Great Britain reserves this item for export to savages.

"Move on, I say! How would you like to be stared at like that yourself?"

regarded as paragons of politeness, but who walk into restaurants ahead of their wives?

"Nonsense!" the Major cried, when I cited this last practice as an evident breach of manners. "We do that for the sake of feminine modesty—to protect our defenseless women against strangers."

"All right . . . but can you deny, you who are reputed to be the best-brought-up people in the world, that your cabinet ministers govern from Westminster with their feet up on the table of the House of Commons?"

"That's a question of privilege, my dear Daninos, not boorishness."

Major Thompson is always right, even when everything conspires to prove him wrong. Here is another of the Englishman's great strengths. He has a ready-made explanation for all those inconsistencies of his countrymen which I, for my part, can only sum up in the word used by the Major to define the French: contradiction.[8]

~~~~~~~~~~~~~~~~~~

[8] Once again this French mania for wanting to explain everything! We English are either far too canny or too thick-headed to try to understand ourselves. Every year, for the past thousand, a foreigner returns home from England with a book intended to explain the English to his countrymen. Which simply proves that not one of them has yet succeeded. There's a good reason for it, too. An Englishman cannot be explained; he can only be taken for granted. The English are like electricity; they exist without anyone being able to explain them. (W.M.T.)

Chapter 2

[P . D .]

CATASTROPHE
AT MRS. CRIPPLESTONE'S

The history of England really began for me the day I blew up the bathroom water-heater (or, to be more exact, the *geyser*) in Mrs. Cripplestone's most respectable Victorian establishment. To tell the truth, had I but known from the start that this strange cylinder of red brass looking like a cross between a boa constrictor and a flame-thrower was called a *geyser*, I would have been on my guard. I would have followed the directions more carefully. But these are things you learn only when the damage is done. In England a foreigner finds out what he should do only after doing what he shouldn't.

It may seem childish to date the kick-off of English

history from the explosion of a water-heater. Most historians prefer to date its start from another catastrophe: the defeat of Harold, King of England, by William the Conqueror in 1066—a year that the British, by one of those strange quirks which so mystify the foreigner, consider the most glorious in their history. But quite aside from the fact that it is indispensable for anyone really wishing to get to know Great Britain to visit one of those boardinghouses where spinsters write personal letters to the editor of *The Times* offering their advice on the castration of cats, or try to make fortunes by betting—grudgingly—on French race-horses at Ascot, it is often easier to explain England by the absence of central heating than by the presence of the Plantagenets.

The golden age of British comfort, on the renown of which the British still live, dates from 43 B.C. In those days Britain could boast both Romans and central heating. The two disappeared at about the same time—the first never to return, the second to be re-adopted only with great hesitancy, usually by owners of modern apartment buildings or cosmopolitan hotels of rather dubious repute.

Now, nothing, you might think, could be more impersonal than a water-heater. On the Continent, no doubt. But English water-heaters are not like others. Like the English themselves, they always keep something from

3 0

you. Of course, if you get to know them well after a good-ish lapse of time, they can become the best friends in the world and warm your water to a chipper 55 degrees. But if the very first day you meet them you become too familiar and light them up like some vulgar continental water-heater, their susceptibilities are offended and they slap you down. You have to remember that you are in a land of compromise; and just as the Anglican Church is a compromise between Catholicism and Protestantism, so the hot water of British boardinghouses is a compromise between ice and steam.

There are, to be sure, plenty of hotels in London where the water is as piping hot as on the Continent. If you are going to England to wash, you had better stay at the Savoy. But that wasn't my sole aim in crossing the Channel, and the Major was perfectly right in advising me to put up at his friend Mrs. Cripplestone's, in South Kensington, in order to catch a glimpse of British life in the raw.

Mrs. Cripplestone's boardinghouse is one of those classical dishes of creamy stucco to which the architects saw fit to add a chunk of Parthenon icing. Under the neo-Grecian entrance, to which you accede by climbing three steps that are religiously white-washed every Monday, is a small brass knocker, glinting at you like a beady eye out of the green door. The simplicity of the cream-colored façade with its sash-windows leaves you unprepared for the maze of dark passages within—a characteristic of so many London dwellings which, unable to grow in height, have expanded laterally into their neighbors. The result is a labyrinth of different floor levels, winding corridors, and surprise staircases such as you get in the Navy. In my room, where the floor sloped gently, the inkwell on the desk had a habit of moving under its own steam along a pre-established course at a speed varying with the weight of the bus-and-truck traffic outside. I had greater trouble getting used to the northeast by southeast drift of the bed, and waking up in the middle of the room, after dropping off to sleep next to the wall, was a disconcerting experience.

Mrs. Cripplestone, who has commanded this terrestrial vessel for the last thirty-five years, seems to be hewn of the same stout timber. Constructed in 1879, added to from 1893 to 1897 thanks to the exertions of the headmistress of Godolphin College,[1] Mrs. Cripplestone was en-

~~~~~~~~~~~~~~~~~~

[1] Miss Eleanor Savernake, famed for having developed a form of *proper deportment* exercise intended to straighten the spines of young girls by having them stand motionless for an hour with a glass of water on their heads. She thus added an inch and a half to the Duchess of Ratigan and an inch to Mrs. Cripplestone.

trusted to the proprietary care of a first mate, Ramsay Dunbar, who died prematurely after losing his fortune between Epsom and Newmarket, and then had the finishing touches put to her by a Colonel of the Indian Army, W. R. S. Cripplestone, who preserved himself on Scotch to a ripe old age.

The two deceased spouses are still hanging—one around Mrs. Cripplestone's neck, the other on her bosom —in two medallions of wrought silver, and the fact that she cannot move without making the Colonel jump in the full-dress uniform of the Bengal Lancers confers on her a singular authority. Her lofty stature, the haughty mien of a sallow countenance whose noble jowls contrast with a battle-ax nose, the souvenirs of close to a century sprinkled over her bodice of Nottingham lace, her long neck held upright by a black ribbon behind which her Adam's apple seems to play a game of hide-and-seek, and her lengthy, severe, purple skirts make Mrs. Cripplestone one of the most authentic monuments of the Victorian age. (Visiting hours: Tuesdays and Thursday, 4 to 6.) Also, the way she has of fixing you with a steely eye from behind her lorgnette of Seychelles (G.B.) tortoise shell contributes in no small degree toward maintaining a truly Spartan discipline in the household.

Here the old ways are still respected. Every morning

at seven o'clock, whether you like it or not, an Irish dragon by the name of Jennifer bursts into your room in her vegetable-green serge dress and her white linen cap to bring you—in the name of the British Empire—the first cup of "early morning tea" which ushers in the English day. Duly answering this matutinal bugle call, the four widows, seven spinsters, and three retired army majors who make up Mrs. Cripplestone's permanent clientele then harness themselves for the second cup of tea, the real one, served downstairs in the dining-room, where, amid tables and sideboards in genuine mahogany, four Indian elephant's feet are stolidly ending their careers as aspidistra pots.

At the noise caused by the explosion of the water-heater, this respectable company was before me in an instant. With my pajamas three quarters burned off by the explosion, my hair disheveled, my face blackened, a flannel towel serving as a hasty loincloth, I had to face these already fully dressed people. Mrs. Cripplestone, after examining me for a moment through her lorgnette, quickly averted her gaze from the hideous and disgusting spectacle I presented.

"Really!" she said, without looking at me. "I don't see how you ever managed such a thing! Mrs. Peacock"—who was standing right behind her, not missing a trick—

After the explosion: hour of reckoning at Mrs. Cripplestone's.

"has been taking two baths a week here ever since 1920, and I have not once had a disturbance of this sort with her. Really, it's quite shocking!"

Shocking, indeed! Mrs. Cripplestone, it turned out, was "afraid" that she would have to send me the plumber's bill, and I soon gathered, without her having to rub it in, that it might be pretty steep. What plagued me, however, was not the prospect of paying the bill, nor even the ridiculous attire Mrs. Cripplestone had caught me in and which had revealed to her lady clients the very first day a secret that many of them might otherwise never have discovered. It was an unbearable guilt complex that overwhelmed me every time I opened the dining-room door and heard people whispering back and forth in a great rustling of sibilants: "Look, it's the Frenchman who blew up the geyser!"

The next few days I was allowed to use the bathroom on the third floor, provided that Jennifer put the machine into operation. But once you have gotten off on the wrong foot with people, it's difficult to regain your balance. Two days after the catastrophe, an unfortunate flick of my bathtowel brought the pink shade of the ceiling light (Regency Period) crashing down on my head.

Unable to stand it any longer, I left Mrs. Cripplestone's boardinghouse the very next day.

Chapter 3

[P . D .]

THE LAND OF HIDE-AND-SEEK

In the United Kingdom everything seems designed to rout the invader, in time of peace as much as in time of war. The camouflaging of street names and house numbers is, of course, a classic weapon employed by General Staffs the world over to disorient enemy parachutists. But the English have adapted it to peacetime purposes with an uncompromising rigor.

For any foreigner with a merely average memory it is next to impossible to retain the full address of an Englishman living in the country. He may well succeed in retaining a piece of:

MAJOR W. MARMADUKE THOMPSON
"The Tower"
Rowland's Castle
Rowland Hill Road
Marlborough Heights
Pendleton, Hampshire

but, considering that none of this is pronounced as it is written, is it surprising that the visitor ends up mislaying a good half of it?

The first thing I learned on reaching Pendleton was that Pendleton was not there, but a little farther on at a place called Fortescue. Coming up onto some heights—those of Marlborough, as I ascertained from a passer-by—I was lucky enough to run into a nameless lane that, I was courteously informed, was called Rowland Hill Road. This lane was bordered on each side by some fifty brick bungalows indistinguishable from one another save by the floral decoration out in front.

In most countries, when they finish a house, the architects go a little farther down the road and try to build another that is different. But in England, when they get through with one house, they don't waste an inch of space and they promptly stick an identical one right next to it—with the same bricks, the same bay window, the same little garden, the same doorway, and the same furniture. In fact, only when he sees his wife's face (assuming he hasn't had a snifter on the way home) can an Englishman be sure he's really home.

Even then he can be none too sure. For it's a funny thing . . . the similarity in their houses seems to have engendered an isomorphism in their inmates. When the Good Lord—the time and weather permitting—lets His eye roam over England around eight a.m., He must see the same man (multiplied by 20 million) leaving the same house via the same garden after conferring the same tender look on the lawn-mower and the same absent-minded kiss on the (left) cheek of the same wife, who, having waved him good-by with her (right) hand, walks back through the same bay-windowed living-room, where the same wild ducks pursue their V-shaped flight in the same painting of Peter Scott's *Sunset on the River,* after which she goes upstairs to make herself up in the same bedroom in front of the same dresser, graced with the same three ornaments —an oval mirror, a brace of hair-curlers, and a perfume bottle marked "Evening in Paris."

On Rowland Hill Road I noticed that certain houses bore names and others numbers—never both—and some nei- ther.

I asked an inhabitant who was busy gardening if he knew Major Thompson's house.

"You mean 'The Castle'?"

"No, 'The Tower.' "

"Yes, that's it!"

And thus it was that I ran the Major to earth in "The Tower," which was really "The Castle," in the township of Pendleton, which was really Fortescue. It was all pretty far afield from Rowland Hill Road, which I had long since left far behind me without ever getting away from it. With its tall brick chimneys, its ivy-covered façade, and its small-paned, lancet windows, the Major's manor house, without being exactly lordly, bore an unmistakable Tudor stamp. Defying the brisk wind blowing over these heights, the Major himself was gardening in gray flannels and a striped blazer, his head bare and a pipe in his mouth. From his face it was clear that this was one of his good days, but the same could not be said for his wife, Martine, whose head, thrust out of a second-story window, seemed about to be guillotined.[1]

[1]The French, who first conceived the idea of making doors into windows, have always been baffled by the latter. Their helplessness, in the face of as harmless a household object as a sash-window, is attested by the title they have conferred on it in their language—*fenêtre à guillotine*. That the French should never have succeeded in taming this utilitarian device is another proof of the basic superiority of British civiliza-

Having disengaged herself more or less, Martine launched into a tirade against this system of aeration.

"Ah! It's a good thing we are only going to be here for a month or two! With these hunting trophies all over the place, I keep hitting my head on an elephant tusk or the jaw of a tiger! Never, never shall I get used to living in this *ménagerie!*"

Whereupon I saw the stuffed head of a black panther sail through the air and land at the feet of the Major, who, upon examination, simply observed:

"Sumatra . . . 1932."

After which, Major Thompson resumed planting his Glorious gladioli, alternating a yellow Nelson with a red Marshal Montgomery in accordance with the advice proffered on the front page of *The Times* by Messrs. Cuthbert and Co., *The Nation's Nurserymen* since 1797.[2]

Visibly exasperated by Marmaduke's phlegmatic calm, Martine burst out of the house and unleashed a broadside against the discomforts of the ancestral mansion.

wwwwwwwwwwwwwwww

tion. The sash-window is a typically Anglo-Saxon invention, offering, as it does, a humane compromise between the windy iciness of the out-of-doors and the stifling airlessness of the indoors. (W.M.T.)

[2] The English language is, no doubt, the only one in the world where the word "nursery" is used to designate both the place where children are raised and where petunias are grown.

"Don't talk to me," she exclaimed, "about your famous British comfort! It's definitely overrated. First, I spend my time freezing . . . and then—"

"That's because you're not properly trained for it, my dear," Major Thompson interrupted. "We British are inured to the cold from childhood. At Rugby I had to chop the ice in my morning tub with a hammer, and I jolly well hope those young bounders are still doing it today.[3] Here in England we grow strong because we are taught to endure the cold, and later on we endure the cold because we are strong."

wwwwwwwwwwwwww

[3] I can vouch for the accuracy of the Major's statement on this point. I have visited a number of British public schools where it is still as freezing as ever. You might almost say that England makes a cult of privation and discomfort. For 2,000 years the British have spent their time chilling themselves, and they have made chilliness one of their threescore and ten religions. Not so long ago two students from Reading spent three nights shivering in a cave on the outskirts of the city, clad only in animal skins and potato sacks—for the simple pleasure of proving that one can live today as men did in prehistoric times. They failed, naturally, to start a fire by rubbing two flints together, and they were reduced to using matches. But, apart from that, their experiment was an unqualified success. They emerged from their cave in Whiteknights Park more dead than alive, but delighted. It all goes to show once again how much the English love to freeze themselves and to walk around coatless, or with a simple trench coat on, when the thermometer registers 5 degrees above—just to defy the elements. So, too, in certain London clubs the temperature is never supposed to rise—even in the dead of winter—above 50 degrees.

"You are speaking nonsense, *mon Marminet*," said Martine, in a softer tone. "You English are more often in bed with your *flu* than we French with our *grippe*. Everybody knows that there is only a *feefty-feefty* chance to have an Englishman keep a rendezvous in winter—not because he is careless, but because half of England is in bed."

"Balderdash!" spluttered the Major.

"Come now! Not only are you always catching colds, but one even has trouble washing in your freezing bathrooms. When I think of the scene you put on at Châteauroux, because there was a tiny little leak in the basin! It is so typical! You explode over the plumbing in Châteauroux, but you do not mind breaking ice in Salisbury—provided it is done in the best Tudor style!"

"Preposterous!" exploded the Major. "At any rate, *we* wash . . . and a good sight more often than certain goosepimpled people who like only hot water! . . . The best proof there is of how seldom the French wash is that they look so much cleaner on Sundays!"

"But on that day you wash even less! . . . Ah, you British and your *esprit de contradiction*.⁴ . . . Yes, and

⁴ The reference is to our alleged love of contradiction and argument. (W.M.T.)

4 3

what about your castles? Your castles are iceboxes where
the coldest room of all is the one where one must strip
naked—the bathroom. And when I think of those awful
blankets of yours that keep one awake with frozen feet.
J'ai horreur de ça!"

"Martine, dear, you French like your comfort in bed.
We like ours seated. I'm never less at ease than in one of
your wretched *salons* in a stiff Louis XVI or Directoire
chair that seems more anxious to throw me out than to take
me in. In France to talk comfortably you have to go to
bed."

"*Ma Marmine* . . . Always that old-fashioned notion
about the bed-loving Frenchman!"

"Well, Katherine Mansfield herself used to say so,
and remember, dear, she wasn't English, she was a New
Zealander. Anyway, in our homes there's always a cosy
corner where you can relax comfortably in a deep armchair
which doesn't make you want to get up and take to your
bed."

"Yes, and it's why your wives get so horribly bored
while you snooze in your sinister clubs pretending to read
in *The Times* about Colonial Office policy in upper *Ubanga*
—"

"Uganda!" the Major corrected.

44

"Ubanga . . . Uganda . . . or whatever it is! But in the meantime I am not going to mold away in this drafty hole much longer. Besides, we must go up to London, if only to take out the Pochets! All we have done for them so far was to see them to their hotel."

There are times when fading away is the better part of discretion. I decided that there was too much electricity in the air at the Major's. The presence of a guest, with Martine in such a frame of mind, could hardly have alleviated the atmosphere. So I used the excuse of an appointment with the Pochets to cut short my visit.

"All the same," I said to Marmaduke, as I took leave of him, "why do you insist on hiding the names of your roads and the numbers of your houses, all so diabolically similar, so that one can never tell where one is?"

"Why in blazes do you need to know, my dear fellow? Either you live there and you know it, or you don't live there and don't need to know it. That way we get some peace in life—except, of course, when chaps like you come along."

It is only fair to remark that things are like this only in the country. In London they are far more complicated. There almost every house, though identical with its neighbors, has a number that is out of step.

Right away I lost a precious lot of time searching for Mrs. Cripplestone's very Victorian establishment in Cavendish Lane, because I stupidly thought of looking for No. 58 between Nos. 56 and 60.

"I'd 'ave a look over 'ere, if I were you," a delivery boy advised me, leading me over to the house next to No. 37.

It sometimes happens, of course, that a number is in its proper place, but after a time in London you get so used to not finding it there that you stop looking for it. As a general rule the numbers don't follow each other consecutively. That would be too monotonous. On one side of the street they go in ascending order, on the other side in descending order. Sometimes they stop descending in order to go up again, only to pause exhausted and resume their descent.

From Tacitus to Diderot and Nietzsche, every writer of note has stressed the fact that the English are melancholic, morose, and gloomy people. Fertile soil indeed for the cultivation of humor—that gay plant watered by sadness! Even when the English laugh, they keep it well concealed. Where, then, have they tucked away their sense of fantasy? At least in part, in the numbering of their houses.

A race of master humorists, the English have managed a miracle—the miracle of real-estate humor. In France a tourist often has the impression that people are laughing at him inside their houses behind the shutters. But in England, where there are no shutters, it is the houses themselves that mock you.

Even the streets are capricious in the extreme. Relax your attention for a moment and you will find that a street has changed its name or lost it completely. Sometimes it loses its name for a minute or two, takes another, and then, after due reflection, goes back to the first.

It can also happen that a main street keeps its surname on the right, after changing its patronymic on the left. It was thus that Pochet got himself raked over the coals by his wife for arriving three hours late at 55 Prince's Gate, which they had forgotten to inform him was to be found in Exhibition Road. Not only does it bore English streets to carry around the same names all the time, but they dislike limiting their meanderings to just one part of town. It's the sportive side of English topography which, by its glorious uncertainty, obeys one of the United Kingdom's basic laws: always give Chance and the weaker fellow his innings. This law is as binding for the fox, which it would be an outrage to shoot, as for Napoleon, whom it would have been unsporting to remove to Saint Helena without promptly founding a secret society dedicated to his rescue.[5]

It is, after all, only fair play that the rolling English road should upset the calculations of the mile-hungry motorist by interposing hedgerows and unexpected rotaries. If there weren't twenty-three High Streets, thirteen King Streets, and eleven Duke Streets in London, what merit would there be in finally running down one's own?

Besides, one must grant the English this: they are very kind. When they see you are lost, they don't hesitate to accompany you until they're lost along with you. Whereupon they entrust you to the care of another helpful citizen or of a policeman, who generally gets you to take the subway or points out your road in an utterly incomprehensible fashion.

Not long after my invasion of "The Tower," Pochet and I

[5] Little known in France, this society had many adherents in Great Britain, where, contrary to what one might think, Napoleon's gaoler, Hudson Lowe, has never enjoyed a good press, whereas the Emperor remains extremely popular. In a poll conducted among twelve-year-old students at a London school by a Professor Frank Dash, it was found that in answer to the question: "Whom do you admire the most?" Napoleon figured at the head of the list, alongside Marshal Montgomery and ahead of Nelson, Churchill, and William the Conqueror.

set out in search of Shrewsbury Place, the site of the resi-
dence of Colonel Basil Cranborne, an old friend of Marmaduke's. It was not long before Pochet was forced to ap-
proach one of those impressive bobbies who look down at
you in the most disconcerting way. Having got the desired
instructions in the nose, so to speak, Pochet came back to
me with dismay written all over his face.

"I'm no better off than I was before. No wonder these
people don't have the same appetite as we. Between meals
they eat half their words. And they've got 450,000 of them.[6]
I didn't catch a word of what that giant said to me, except,
of course, 'You can't miss it!' I occasionally get lost on my
own, but when an Englishman says to me: 'You can't miss
it,' I'm *sure* to get lost."

Even the English get lost in their labyrinths, and how
could it be otherwise?

As we were looking for Shrewsbury Place and had
finally turned into Shrewsbury Avenue, we could expect
at any moment to run the Place down. But in England a
Place is everything but a place. A Place is a square. A
Square, however, can be a close. And a Close, as often as

[6] To be exact, 455,000 words in the *Oxford English Dictionary*, as
against 70,000 words in the *Grand Larousse* and 40,000 in the *Diction-
naire de l'Académie.*

not, can be a short street. One thing does at any rate simplify matters—you can be sure that a Terrace will never be a terrace. It will be just another street. So why rack your brains over it? You have to be afflicted with the wretched logic of a continental to insist on finding a garden where the address reads Gardens or a gate where it reads Gate. And when you think that there are sixty-five different words for a street in England, why on earth should they simply call it a "street"? It's much jollier to call it a "mews" or a "crescent."

"Well," groaned Pochet, exhausted, "what would you say to a drink?"

We were lucky enough to run down a pub that was still open.[7] But hardly had we ordered a couple of whiskys when we were asked to gulp them down immediately:

"You've just three more minutes to finish your drinks," the gentleman bottle-washer informed us.

At this announcement a good score of clients rushed out and across the street to another pub opposite ours, which closed a half-hour later. The two sides of the street belonged, we discovered, to two different municipal boroughs, so that their hours of closing and even their street-

[7] The Public Houses in England are allowed to serve liquors from 11.00 a.m. to 3.00 p.m. and from 6.00 p.m. to 10.00 or 10.30 p.m., depending on their locality or city district.

lighting were different. The pavement on our side was lit by gaslight, and on the other side by neon.

"Can I take a bottle of whisky with me?" Pochet inquired.

" 'Ere, 'ave a look at the licensing rules!" we were told.

The licensing rules read as follows:

1. *Consumers may not take any form of spirits with them outside the hours of lawful consumption.*
2. *Any order given during lawful opening hours may be de-delivered at home outside of the lawful hours.*
3. *Any order made from outside during the closing hours may be delivered at home outside of closing hours if a period of opening hours has occurred in the interim.*[8]

"All right," said Pochet, "give me some aspirin instead."

It wasn't a joke. Pochet had indeed acquired a headache. Leaving the pub, he stepped in at a "chemist's" to buy some aspirin and, while he was about it, some toothpaste. The pharmacist agreed to sell him the aspirin, but as for the toothpaste, which he had right next to him, the

wwwwwwwwwwwww

[8] From this it can be deduced—more or less clearly—that, while you cannot take a bottle of whisky out once the pub has closed its doors, you can have the bottle follow you if you can get someone to bring it to your domicile.

legal hour was up. . . . Pochet thus learned that in the United Kingdom there is an hour for headaches and another for brushing one's teeth.

"*Mon Dieu!*" he sighed. "What a country!"

It was late indeed when we finally found Colonel Basil Cranborne's house. The calling card I had with me indicated the "ground floor," so I rang the doorbell on the street level. An elderly lady came to open it.

"Colonel Cranborne?"

"It's upstairs."

"But isn't this the ground floor?"

"No, it's the basement."

"And the ground floor?"

"Climb the steps. I think you'll find it's inhabited," added the old lady.

I gathered from this odd dialogue that in certain London houses, if you are told that the ground floor is inhabited, it means that they're receiving on the second.

A good bit of this confusion could be obviated, no doubt, if we could only reach some kind of *entente* on words. But here, again, the English do their damnedest to mystify the foreigner. The English have borrowed some 32,500 words from abroad and never bothered to return them; and, not content merely to keep them, they have given them an entirely new twist. Once a French term is confiscated by the English language, it acquires a meaning quite different from, if not completely opposite to, the one you expect. And if, out of friendship, the French borrow a few English words to enrich their own vocabulary, the English promptly assert that such words no longer mean anything to them—such as the word *footing,* which the French use to designate a good leg-stretching walk (*faire du footing*), but which means nothing the other side of the Channel.[9] How can one ever understand a people who use the word *grand,* but don't mean something big; who say a *merchantman* when they mean a cargo vessel, and a *vessel* when they mean a jug; who use the word *habit* to designate not a costume, but a custom; who insist on using a yard that contains 914 millimeters, a pound that equals 450 grams at one moment and 480 the next, a ton that oscillates between 1,016 and 907 kilograms, and an ounce that has one value for the pharmacist and another for the grocer? All of this is part of that elaborate camouflage intended to

<hr/>

[9] Let us forget all this tall talk about French generosity and English rapacity and ask ourselves in all seriousness what one is to think of a people who call a thousand million a *billion* and a billion a *trillion;* an umbrella a *parapluie* and a parasol an *ombrelle;* a cap a *casquette,* and a casket a *coffret;* a chat a *causerie* and a cat a *chat;* a parrot a *perroquet* and a parakeet a *perruche;* who call a magpie a *pie,* a pie a *tarte,* and a tart a *grue.* (W.M.T.)

hamstring the foreigner with such diabolic inventions as cricket, the secret aim of which is to be so obscure that it will give any alien attempting to understand it a headache and drive him to drink once he thinks he has unraveled its secrets.

"When I think," Mme Pochet exclaimed to me, "of the trouble I had finding out that a pound contains 20 shillings, a shilling 12 pence, and a half crown 2 shillings and 6 pence! And all to what purpose? So that I could walk into a shop to buy a Cashmere cardigan and have the price thrown at me in guineas, a form of currency that hasn't existed for 138 years, but which is still worth slightly more than a pound. *Ah, non! Quel casse-tête!*"

Chapter 4

[P . D .]

THE PURSUIT OF PRECEDENT
or
"The Strange Case of the Intrusive Egg"

One of the marked superiorities the English enjoy over other peoples is their ability to imbue the foreigner with a crippling inferiority complex the moment he sets foot on British soil—indeed, even before he arrives.

The Pochets were overjoyed at the prospect of being able to make their entry into Great Britain with Major Thompson. But this entry was made through two quite different doors. The Major, as a British subject, was already freely treading the soil of Albion while they, as "aliens," were being carefully screened.

Now this word "alien" has a singularly exasperating effect on Mme Pochet.

"*Tout de même,* we're not lepers, are we? When I think that these people call themselves the most civilized in the world! You could perfectly well get here by subway, but no! the English force you to get seasick or airsick on the way—and all on account of a mere puddle of water which would hardly stretch from Paris to Versailles! And the result? You arrive deflated."

She had barely got these words off her chest when Her Majesty's Customs officials confiscated her white poodle, Virgule, because, as a continental dog, she could enter the United Kingdom only after a six-month quarantine. As everyone knows, ever since 1885 (cf. Pasteur) French dogs have been mad. And as Virgule, unnerved by the commotion, forgot herself on the red base of a Royal Mail box, the Customs man added: "We'll teach her to behave herself properly. . . ." [1]

The leave-taking from Virgule, accomplished under

[1] The English claim that their dogs, disciplined from the tenderest age, are better brought up than other dogs. There must be something in the English air which makes the dogs there behave more properly than on the Continent. Perhaps it's the way their owners have of addressing them like gentlemen, by saying, for example: "Will you kindly leave the room, Master Dick!"

the impassive stare of the British immigration officers, was a heart-rending spectacle. Mme Pochet was all ready to re-embark.

"You might at least have warned me, Major," she said to Marmaduke.

"I thought you knew," said the Major, who on hear-ing Mme Pochet's cries of distress had made a momentary sortie from the United Kingdom and an unexpected entree into the no man's land of aliens.

Mme Pochet made one final attempt to circumvent the Cerberus of Customs officialdom.

"I demand you, please . . ." she began.

The immigration officer took the request very badly.

" 'I demand' means *'j'exige,'* " the Major explained. "Hardly ever used here. Say 'I ask.' "

"Je n'askerai rien," said Mme Pochet. "That's just too much!"

While Mme Pochet was thus being divested of Virgule, Pochet was having troubles of his own with the police. The first question an "alien" is asked on entering the United Kingdom is: "How long are you going to stay?" Which is tantamount to asking: "When are you thinking of leaving?" The second question is: "What are you coming over here to do?" These two questions are enough to unsettle the most innocent soul. One of Her Majesty's immigration officers has only to ask me what I have come to England for, and I no longer know myself. The most inoffensive visit thus immediately assumes an alarming character to Scotland Yard. But it is just as dangerous to try to browbeat your way through by answering, as did that inveterate joker, Pochet:

"If anyone asks you, *mon ami,* just tell them you don't know."

Whereupon he burst into a hearty laugh which the stiff-faced official vis-à-vis did not seem to appreciate. Pochet was forthwith handed a list of articles banned by Her Majesty's Customs. Beneath the emblem of the Lion and the Unicorn, he noticed that a solemn interdiction was placed on the importation of parrots, muskrat, and leg of mutton (unless pre-cooked on the Continent).

This childish fear of not-to-be-committed crimes overwhelms the foreigner the moment he sets foot on British soil and it does not relinquish him until he has left the country. There is—at any rate, for the Continental—something almost adulterous in this sense of insecurity. If you are a married man hastening to a secret assignation you find your route encumbered with placid strollers, children in hand, or with citizens with limpid consciences, never straying from the beaten path that leads from home to office, whose unclouded gaze seems to lay bare the sinner's lust for debauch. Here 53 million citizen-policemen[2] look with a disapproving eye at the agile Latin who moves up ten places in the queue, thereby breaking a fundamental law of behavior which the English would never think of circumventing: The Rule! Stricter than any code engraved in marble is that unwritten, phantom law—Tradition—which, with anthracite, is Great Britain's most precious raw material.

Wherever you may walk, or stop, or breathe in England you can feel the weight of a thousand years of history bearing down on you—the maximum of historical density being concentrated in the Tower of London, with its walls sweating the blood of princes and that grim dungeon where Edward IV had his brother drowned in a butt of malmsey.

The English love to make telephone calls in eighteenth-century sedan chairs, to sip a tomato juice in

[2] Little more than a century ago the English acted as their own police. This habit is as evident in their sense of discipline as in their affection for the behelmeted bobbies, the only policemen in the world who are not armed. (They owe their appellation to the first name of their creator, Sir Robert Peel.)

an inn founded in 1135, to sit down at a sixteenth-century table to savor Elizabethan cucumbers,[3] and to have pointed out to them in Gothic lettering the way to the

𝕷𝖆𝖛𝖆𝖙𝖔𝖗𝖞.

One day when I was in the Haymarket I walked into a tobacconist's and asked for some tobacco. Instantly I knew I had made a mistake. You just don't walk into Fribourg and Treyer, Tobacconists, Established in 1720, and ask for tobacco as you would in a shop on the Champs Elysées. The gentleman behind the counter couldn't have been more shocked if I had asked him for a waffle. Tobacco? Of course, but what kind of tobacco?

"If you want to," Major Thompson—who was with me—whispered into my ear, "you can ask for Waterloo Mixture or Wingate Mixture, or for any other of the many blends that Fribourg and Treyer have handed down from father to son and inscribed in their books for their customers since 1720. You can, like Beau Brummel, Mrs. Sid-

~~~~~~~~~~~~~~~~

[3] The publicity folder for the Gore Hotel (in South Kensington) invites you to dine in the Elizabethan room "like Falstaff 366 years ago," and to be treated to the same "provocative service [waitresses dressed in sixteenth-century décolleté costumes] which our lords and masters once enjoyed."

dons, or Disraeli, order a mixture of Masulipatam and Latakia, but, for the love of God, don't just ask for tobacco! Do I call the sommelier at the Tour-d'Argent and ask him for red wine? Why not try my favorite mixture? It's William Pitt's."

So even when the Major smokes, it's a puff of history that he draws from his pipe.

As we were not too far from St. James's Street and Pochet wanted to buy a hat, we made for Lock's venerable shop (established 1759). In the window was a display, like the flags of the Invalides in Paris, of glorious, threadbare trophies of the past (such as the nineteenth century's first bowler hat).

Pochet had his hand on the doorknob, when the Major said to him: "Nelson, my dear Pochet, used to open this very same door."

An evocation like this when you are about to enter a hat shop is enough to turn the soberest head. Later Pochet confided to me that he had felt his soft gray hat literally wilt with humility over his ears. After pausing for a moment inside to examine a bill (carefully kept under glass) that His Grace the Duke of Bedford had paid in 1760, Pochet submitted his cranium to the mercies of a solemn-faced salesman, who gazed with dismay at the strange and foreign thing the visitor was wearing on his head.

"I would like to buy a bowler hat," Pochet announced.

"We don't sell bowlers, Sir," the salesman answered. "We fit them."

The clerk disappeared, then returning and thrust down on Pochet's startled brow the still-warm form of a bowler hat, which in a few seconds turned as hard as wood. Five minutes later, and for the first time in his life, Pochet walked out with a date—1759—on his head.

The English do not simply have a passion for the old. One of their favorite sports is the hunt for precedents.[4] Whenever something new occurs in England, the first concern of the English is to determine if such a thing has ever happened before. Suppose, for example, that the Arsenal football team scores three goals in four minutes. Two thousand and five hundred sports writers will immediately

wwwwwwwwwwwwww

[4] Nothing could better attest the real affection lavished by the English on all that is old than the example of a friend of Marmaduke's, a certain Dr. Robinson, whom I went to consult. On each visit I was startled to see a 1925 Rolls-Royce with carefully polished chrome plating stationed in front of his door. I asked him if he knew the owner of this immobile vehicle. "I am the owner," he told me. "But wouldn't you like to turn this one in for a more recent model?" I asked. "To tell you the truth," he answered, "the car I use is in a garage behind the house. This one doesn't run, but it impresses my patients."

burrow feverishly into the dust-covered almanacs in pursuit of a precedent. Now suppose you stop your car in the middle of Westminster Bridge at noon. No doubt you will have some words with the police. However, if you can furnish proof that by virtue of a privilege of the Crown your ancestor the Earl of Sherborne was entitled in 1496 to halt his carriage in the middle of the bridge, you stand a good chance of winning your case.[5]

It took the English a century and a half to realize that the Grenadier guard stationed in front of No. 10 Downing Street 167 years earlier, after an attempt on Walpole's life, was no longer needed.

English justice itself is founded on precedents. There is no written code of law, but only collections of precedents which the Justices refer to. When no precedent exists, one is often created, but it's quite a to-do. One of the most recent and typical cases was that involving William Joyce, who was brought to trial for having made treasonable broadcasts over the Nazi radio under the name of "Lord Haw-Haw." Not being British either by birth or by adop-

wwwwwwwwwwwwwww

[5] A Professor of International Law once provoked an uproar at the University of London by presenting a thesis in French. When his colleagues objected that this was contrary to the established usage, he replied that he had based his action on a decree dating from 1116. Everyone was delighted.

tion, Joyce did not—according to his defense counsel—owe allegiance to the Crown. The prosecution argued that he did, since he was the holder of a British passport. The question was thus to determine whether the holder of a British passport becomes by the same token British. No one could answer the question, for precedents had been looked for in vain. After a long session, Mr. Justice Tucker made legal history by deciding that Joyce owed obedience to the Crown by virtue of his passport. Today this is part of the common law. Joyce himself was hanged.

Whereas the new upsets the British, precedents reassure them. They track down old dates as we do rabbits. At heart they dislike doing anything that hasn't been done at least once since 1066. Perhaps this explains why so many English women die old maids.

While the French, armed with their *Littrés* and their *Larousses*, wage strenuous verbal battles to determine whether one should say *"le Normandie," "la Normandie,"* or simply *"Normandie,"* the English, less given to syntactical skirmishes, carry on mighty wars of dates.

The Times is a particularly choice arena for such jousts. Not long ago a certain Mr. N. J. Lambert (42 Baker St., London, W.1.) wrote to the editor of this venerable daily to call his attention to the unwonted presence of a fried egg in the "mixed grill" served to him by a West

End restaurant. Never, to his knowledge, had such an incongruity been perpetrated before. But an Englishman should know that one should never say "Never." For several days later *The Times* published a letter by Mr. J. P. Gabbatt (Durford Edge, Petersfield, Hampshire) citing the presence of such an egg in a mixed grill as early as 1922 in Cambridge. This was the start of a great wave of opinion. For weeks five hundred thousand Englishmen were passionately aroused by the column in *The Times* entitled "The Intrusive Egg." Mr. Kevin Fitzgerald (Flat 3, 30 Cadogan Place, London, S.W.1) seems to have had the last word, reporting a poached egg spotted by a shocked Englishman in a mixed grill in Dublin in 1918.[6]

For those readers who may doubt the authenticity of this story, I offer this facsimile of the first two letters published by *The Times* under the title: "The Intrusive Egg."

wwwwwwwwwwww

[6] I might add that I, too, succumbed to the fever of research and succeeded in unearthing a reference to a similar egg among the parchments of one of my ancestors, a contemporary of the Black Prince. *The Times,* however, was unwilling to accept this case as a valid precedent, the mixed grill not having been an established culinary feature at the time of the Hundred Years' War. Too bad! But how, in the face of such an astonishing display of interest, can anyone seriously claim that the British aren't interested in the art of cooking? But this is a subject about which I have some things of my own to say, and which, to the detriment of Pochet and with the permission of Daninos, I shall need more than a footnote to expound. (W.M.T.)

6 5

THE INTRUSIVE EGG

To The Editor of The Times

SIR,

By whose culinary quirk has the fried egg become an ingredient of the mixed grill? This astonishing spectacle has confronted me recently at a famous West End restaurant, a not-so-famous Fleet Street one, and a popular club where they ought to know better. Let us banish the interloper from our dining-table before it appears floating poached in the turtle soup.

Yours faithfully,
N. J. LAMBERT
42 Baker Street, W.1.

THE INTRUSIVE EGG

To The Editor of The Times

SIR,

The protest of your correspondent Mr. Lambert, whether justified or not, seems a little belated. In my own experience the mixed grill of a certain Cambridge hotel was always topped by a fried egg as early as 1922.

I have the honour to be, Sir, your obedient servant,
J. P. GABBATT
Durford Edge,
Petersfield, Hampshire

66

Chapter 5

[W . M . T .]

WITH POCHET IN BRITAIN

Whenever I travel with Pochet, there are always more than two of us along—a phenomenon that, for an Englishman, at any rate, is not a little disconcerting. For Pochet is never alone when he leaves his native France; a ghost accompanies him. His is not a spirit akin to our noble phantoms of Scotland and Cornwall; it is a less aristocratic one in the shape of beefsteak and French fries. It is, nonetheless, an obsessive ghost, not to say a devouring one.

A couple of hours cannot go by in London, or, indeed, elsewhere, without Pochet's suddenly feeling himself haunted by this ghost, which reduces him to a state of piteous servitude.

"Ah, I'd give anything for a *bon bifteck et pommes frites,*" he says, adding a moment afterward: "You know, a really good one, *comme on le fait chez nous.*" [1]

Pochet is the living proof of the Frenchman's enslavement to his stomach (to say nothing of his liver, an organ which he never stops talking about, but which we British have never admitted to polite society). There is, indeed, no stranger spectacle than that of Pochet wandering through the streets of Piccadilly in a desperate search for a *châteaubriant* or even, incredible as it may sound, for a *guignolet-kirsch.* It's no earthly use my telling him that when it comes to steak, we can hold our own.

"You lent us the word, I'll grant you," he says, "but it's we who make the dish."

Heavens! If only he would make some effort to adapt himself to foreign cooking (without, of course, attaining our degree of ease, since everywhere abroad we are certain of eating better than at home), things would go more smoothly. But Pochet is convinced that France is the only place where people know how to eat. That's all there is to it. I must say, though, that things are not always made to ease his path. The other day in a West End restaurant he was baffled by a menu that gave him a choice

[1] "As we do it at home."

"I'm sorry, Sir, we aren't here to give advice, we're here to serve!"

between two *plats du jour:* Lancashire Hot Pot and Irish Stew. So he asked the advice of the waitress, one of those blue-faced matrons, in a mauve uniform and a white serving-cap, who smacked more of a hospital than of the *haute cuisine.*

"What would you advise me to take?" asked Pochet in his jolly way. "Lancashire Hot Pot or Irish Stew?"

"I am sorry, Sir, we aren't here to give advice, but to serve," the waitress replied.

Somewhat put off by this rejoinder, Pochet plumped arbitrarily for the Lancashire Hot Pot, which, if I may say so, went down badly with his French digestive system. He then declared to me in a sour mood that in France the waiter would have been delighted by such a question and would immediately have unfolded his own *petite idée* as to what was good and what was not. After which he went on to complain that people who devour kippered herring and kidneys when they get up in the morning cannot possibly furnish any useful advice as to what to eat at lunchtime; that we British are quite content to naturalize in boiling water all that we get from abroad—everything from our famous "Roast Beef of Old England" (which we get from the Argentine) to our Canterbury Lamb (from New Zealand) and our Brussels Sprouts, for which we reserve a positively inhuman treatment; and, finally, that because we don't eat properly at mealtimes, we consume between meals the world's greatest quantity of chocolates and sweets.

I never reply to insults, especially when they are justified. My country's cooking is in the image of itself—surrounded by water. That is why I so often take Pochet to London restaurants where French, Italian, and Chinese chefs dispense an excellent British cuisine. But even then Pochet is not satisfied. The moment something is put down on his plate, he thinks of something that isn't there. The first question he asked me when I took him to an Indian restaurant on Swallow Street to taste the curried lamb of my beloved Punjab was: "Do you like the Chinese?"

I was startled by the question and told him I had nothing in particular against them.

"No," said Pochet, "I mean Chinese cooking."

Whereupon he launched into such a succulent description of a Cantonese rice dish he was in the habit of eating in the rue Erlanger that it completely neutralized the taste of the curry. It occurred to me that he might be happier in a Chinese restaurant in Soho. But hardly had he begun attacking his duck *laqué* when he was off on a mouth-watering evocation of a particular *couscous*[2] he had eaten on the rue Montyon. With this mania of his for transporting me to North Africa when I want to take him to China, or to China when I want to take him to India, I end up no longer knowing where I am or what I am eating!

I must admit that even when I am in Paris and at his house I find myself in much the same straits, thanks to that strange game of musical dishes ("Give me some of your white meat and I'll give you a piece of the back") which the French play at the dinner table, making it im-

~~~~~~~~~~~~~~~~

[2] A North African dish made of semolina and bits of lamb.

7 1

possible for me to be master of my own chicken. Having helped herself to a drumstick, Mme Pochet is suddenly tempted by some white meat on her husband's plate, while he is busy transferring a bit of his liver to my plate, saying: "Have a taste of this, Major!" On one occasion, I recall, I had to sit by and watch half my bacon disappear because *Belle-Maman* wanted a bit of it, only to be recompensed by having Pochet Junior's sweetbreads land on my plate. This habit of sticking your fork into your neighbor's plate to scoop up a morsel or deposit a tidbit is unknown in Britain, where we take as little relish in poaching on our neighbor's plate as we do in consuming what is on our own.

That is why when I'm in France and want to savor a tasty eel stew I prefer being alone. For if Pochet is with me, he will immediately start talking about the best eel stew he ever tasted in his life:—"It was in Bordeaux, in '38 . . . no, '37, *chez la mère Musignard* . . ."—and my stew will suddenly seem to have lost all its savor.

Yes, Pochet will certainly never get used to England—no more than Martine or my good friend Daninos. More's the pity!

I remember, back in the days of my tender youth—if one can so refer to an English youth more typified by canings than by any *chouchoutage*[3]—that once, when I was returning from Italy with my father, he took me up on deck and, pointing toward the pale white cliffs emerging from the fog, cried: "Look, my son! The cliffs of Dover! I feel safe at last."

And he breathed in a deep lungful of bracing British air. He was happy to have escaped unharmed from the Mediterranean world. He was about to regain the only possible land on earth—England.

Well, it's just the opposite with Martine and Pochet. The moment they set foot in the United Kingdom they recoil. Pochet recently told me so himself in one of those strange confession-monologues to which the French are oftentimes addicted:

"There's nothing to be done about it, Major! It's no use my walking around with an eighteenth-century date on my hat. My skull just isn't British, and it never will be. I try, like you, to start up a conversation by casually remarking:

‿‿‿‿‿‿‿‿‿‿‿‿

[3] An untranslatable French word that refers not, as one might think at first sight, to the delicacies of the French cuisine, but to a French mother's caresses, characterized by such gentle cooings as *"mon pauvre chou," "mon petit chou"* (my poor darling, my little darling). That the French should have chosen as tough, not to say as British, a vegetable as the cabbage as a substantive of endearment is one of the sublime illogicalities that characterize this supposedly so-logical people.

"The best eel stew. . . . It was in Bordeaux, in '38 . . . no, '37."

'Do you think the situation in Tanganyika should be regarded as very serious?' I make repeated efforts to handle my umbrella as you do, to keep my elbows glued to my sides, and to sip my tea like a gentleman, but it's no good. Your countrymen have a way of behaving and dressing and speaking, and of not speaking, unlike anyone else. I suppose that is why I have the ceaseless impression that I am being mercilessly scrutinized by people who think to themselves: 'He's not a member of the club!'

"Yes, Major, exclusive though it is, England is an enormous club, a club in which everything is a club, from the public school to the House of Lords, the Navy, and the Court, a club of 53 million members who out of a hundred different ways of doing things have chosen the most difficult and, having trained themselves at it for centuries, can now sit back and watch the foreigner make a fool of himself. Look at the boys at Harrow! It's difficult enough to keep on a straw hat, as they do, by perching it forward on top of their noses. They could easily hold them on by passing the elastic under the chin; instead, they stretch it over the back of the neck.

"An Englishman can perfectly well walk around with a leek in his buttonhole, and it will hardly be noticed, since it might be some custom dating from 1687. The other evening I saw a man in white trunks and a striped gym-shirt jogging down Bayswater Road at five o'clock in the afternoon. Imagine a Parisian trotting around the Place de l'Opéra in his shorts at six thirty! One thing is certain—at six thirty-five he would be explaining his strange behavior to the nearest Commissariat de Police. But in Bayswater Road no one ever turned to stare. Tied up though they were in a traffic jam, those Londoners sitting placidly in their buses and cars did not pay the slightest attention to this fellow countryman who was overtaking them at a jog-trot. Some Englishman must have started jogging around London in 1705, so that ever since it has been a normal thing to do.

"I might add," Pochet went on, warming to his theme, "that there is not a country in the world where people spend more time disguising themselves. Here every-one seems to be in uniform—even the civilians. And every-body, at every hour of the day, seems to be carrying out some ritual. In France people can get into uniforms, but the civilian in them still comes out. The man on leave is always discernible beneath the uniform of the soldier. The bus conductor, you feel, is anxious to get rid of his ticket-puncher and to be able to putter around again in his shirt sleeves. The *sergent de ville* who knocks off his tour of duty at the stroke of seven in the morning, to return to his *pot-au-feu,* has already ceased to be a *sergent de ville.* But here in England the uniform makes the person. It im-pregnates him, it absorbs him. The "beefeaters" of the Tower of London seem never to have carried anything but halberds, and one has difficulty imagining the Lord Mayor of London doffing his silver chain to put on his pajamas. From the small boys in top hats and the young girls in mortarboards and black gowns to Sir Winston Churchill in the flowing robes, the English never stop dressing up—except, of course, on just those occasions when we French do so. None, therefore, of our black crepe veils and mourning clothes which in England would be taken as signs of ostentation!

"This impression of not being a 'member of the family' I felt particularly strongly the other night at that gala evening you got me invited to at His Grace the Duke of Sutherland's (P.C., K.T.), whose title goes back, you say, to the thirteenth century. In addition to a multitude of blue-blooded baronets, there were present the Marquesses —I was about to say of Cholmondeley—"

"Chumley," I corrected him.

"Chumley, as you say, with that passion you British have for leaving only half of a word after you have sneezed it out, and Sal'sbury, which is liquefied when pronounced. But the foreign guests were clustered particularly thickly around the Duke of Somerset, no doubt because he has the advantage of having a name that is pronounced almost as it is written.

"Lost in the dense forest of family trees, in the midst of all these people who had let themselves slide down from branch to branch since 1066, I experienced the unsettling sensation of having nothing to hang on to and of being the only one of my century present. Besides, you showed me

The Englishman goes to school disguised as a member of the Stock Exchange . . .

dresses up as a young boy at the university . . .

gets married in uniform . . .

does his military (secret) service in the robes of a false sheik . . .

wears his schoolboy best to go to the Stock Exchange . . .

dons a medieval garb for public functions . . .

enters the House of Lords in an ermine cape, but is . . .

amazed to see continentals disguised for no good reason.

yourself, *cher Major,* how in *Whitaker's Almanac* a mere
twenty lines separate the former Prince of Wales from his
Welsh ancestor Trahaern ap Caradog (1075). So, too,
with the members of your club, who seem ever ready to
climb into their own portrait frames and to take their
places alongside of the Earl of Derby or the Duke of Westminster, draped in their great black robes. When, at your
kind invitation, I penetrated into this mausoleum,[4] I found
that to become a member I would have to give a written
affirmation of my support of the Declaration of 1832 in
favor of the abolition of the Corn Laws. That these laws
had, in fact, been repealed some 123 years before was of
no importance; what was wanted was my opinion in 1832.
Not everyone has the privilege of reversing the gears of
history and declaring his solidarity with the new tend-
encies of a hundred years before.

"And so, Major, in the presence of the many-cen-
turied guests of the Duke of Sutherland, I, who was born
simply when I came into the world, felt naked as a newborn babe. An uncomfortable feeling that I experience
not only in your drawing-rooms, but even on your high-
ways. The other day, while driving toward Bristol, I

----

[4] Pochet meant the Reform Club, where I like to bury myself of an
evening when in London.

8 0

was about to pass a bright red truck when my eye caught a sign on the back of it:

YOU ARE FOLLOWING

WINDHAM AND JOHNSON

Purveyors to Her Majesty
Established 1815

Obviously, if I had read instead:

PICHONNET

Viandes

[*Charente-Maritime*]

it would not have had the same effect on me. It was as though Napoleon had suddenly appeared between my front fender and the truck's exhaust pipe. Traditionally sown with obstacles, the English road now seemed more treacherous than ever. The memory of Waterloo forced me to beat a retreat. If I had had an accident, just think what a figure I would have cut!

"No, it's no use trying to overtake people who got off to a head start in 1815.

"But, to get back to that *soirée* at the Duke of Sutherland's, all this was something I understood much better as a result of following the conversation that evening. For do you know, *mon cher Major,* what it was that everyone was talking about in soft, velvet tones that cushioned all but the sharpest-edged consonants? They were talking of the weather! In France we speak of the weather, *bien sûr*, but then we go on to something else. But here you don't go on. You stick with the weather. The particular topic of conversation that evening was the damnable weather there had been at the time of the last coronation. There was one aged lord there who rattled off a list of all his coronations in terms of the weather at each. 'For Edward VII it rained the evening before . . .' and so on.

"Before long the great question at issue was whether there had ever been a wetter coronation than Edward the Confessor's. When everyone had finally agreed around eleven o'clock that Edward's was the wettest, a long silence, woven of venerable traditions and affinities, engulfed the drawing-room. The conversation seemed to have died out once and for all. And then someone had the *maladresse* to wish to revive it. It was my wife, Solange, who thought she was doing the proper thing. There was, as you may imagine, stupefaction on all sides, but it was quickly shattered by the arrival of a dust-covered and panting archer.

" 'I return from Agincourt,' said the man in the coat of mail. '1415,' he added.

"Then he shot off an arrow, which whizzed through

The wettest coronation since Edward the Confessor's.

the air and woke me. For I had finally dozed off to sleep. Now don't think, *Major*, that this happened because I had not come properly prepared for the evening. Take the question of the coronation. I had carefully learned by

heart the number of diamonds in the Imperial Crown—
2,783, to be exact—and even the number of silkworms
that had spun cocoons for the Queen's robe—52,500. Indeed, I had grown so used to seeing Her Most Gracious
Majesty, in the intimacy of magazines, playing with Prince
Charles on the age-old lawns of Windsor, or saying good-
night to Princess Anne, that I had acquired the impression
that I was one of the family. So much so that I even began
to wonder why I had not been invited to visit them.

"But no! I am not ripe enough for that yet . . . and
I think I never shall be. I should have been wary of people
who when learning to speak begin by biting their tongues,
and who when eating peas use the back of the forks as a
tray on which to heap little piles with the aid of a knife.
I have repeatedly tried to do it, but each Operation *Petit
Pois,* like Operation Teacup (an exercise in balancing a
teacup on the knee), has ended in total defeat. I realized
this the other day when lunching with you at Mrs. Cripplestone's. Inevitably my *petit pois*—so hard and un-*petit*
in England—kept tumbling back onto my plate with a metallic sound. It was no good, *mon cher Major,* your chilling
Mrs. Cripplestone's blood with a tender account of how the
Malays get rid of their enemies by chopping tiger whiskers
into their soup, which then harden in the intestines and
perforate the peritoneum. Mrs. Cripplestone kept one ea-

gle eye on me all the time. And once I had forgotten to pass the claret in a clockwise direction, I was a marked man.

"And then there is this question of hands. *'Tes mains, Alfred, tes mains!'* Solange is always saying to me, on the pretext that I gesticulate too much. For my part, I do not understand what you English do for gestures. You hardly ever use your hands at all. So here is another habit that I must renounce. And *tout compte fait*, Major, I wonder if the best way to behave properly in England isn't to go first to Italy, learn to do everything like the Italians, and then come back and do just the opposite."

Chapter 6

CITIZEN-PETS

For a long time I used to wonder whether in getting to know the English well it wasn't better to be a zoologist than a psychologist. Today I am convinced of it.

This conviction is one I finally acquired on an English train where, like many other passengers, I was obliged to stand in the corridor because the seats in the compartments were occupied by dogs. Now if I were to read nonsense like this in a book, I would promptly dash off an outraged letter to the author to ask if he was trying to pull my leg. But I can personally guarantee the authenticity of this story, and, since just my word for it may seem insufficient,

I shall take the precaution of wrapping it in a piece of the *Daily Telegraph,* the reliable British daily that reported the facts.

The facts are as follows:

On the 2nd of February 1955, with York as our destination, the Pochets and I boarded the Edinburgh Express, which leaves King's Cross Station in London at 10.30 P.M. The train seemed jam-packed, but when we got aboard we discovered that many people were standing in the corridors outside compartments that were full of dogs but empty of passengers.

After a moment's hesitation and with that deplorable tendency the French have for making a public exhibition of themselves, Mme Pochet decided to invade one of the compartments. A long-haired greyhound was stretched out the entire length of one side, while the seats opposite were occupied by a pug, two poodles, and a fifty-year-old lady who, by a trick of mimicry common among people who spend all their time with animals, had the head of a mastiff.

"Can you not push this dog over a bit so that I can sit down?" Mme Pochet asked the mastiff-lady.

"Pamela has her ticket, Madam."

"Of course, but only for *one* seat."

"No, for the entire side!"

"But, after all, you are not going to tell me that if I push your animal a *leetle* . . . like this?"

The instant Mme Pochet touched the sleek hind-quarters of the noble beast with the tip of her umbrella, the mastiff-lady emitted a shrill yelp that rang through the entire train like an alarm signal.

"Please stop at once! Don't you know what dog it is you're disturbing? I'm going to complain to the conductor."

Which is precisely what she did.

A moment later Mme Pochet learned that the beast she had disturbed was none other than Pamela of Quernmore, a Kurdish greyhound and the "supreme champion" of the United Kingdom. Thus, though the seats were indeed occupied by dogs, they weren't just any old dogs. They were the cream of the dog world, who had left their domains in Yorkshire and Scotland and come down to London to win the most treasured laurels in the canine world—the prizes at the Cruft's Show.

"A dog like that, Ma'am," said the conductor, thrusting out his chin in the direction of Pamela of Quernmore, "is worth a million any day." And it was quite clear from the look he then bestowed on Mme Pochet that he rated this foreign lady at a far lower figure.

"*Ah! ça c'est trop fort!*" Mme Pochet exploded. "Not only do they ask me to stand up in the presence of seated dogs, but then they practically fine one! Go on traveling in this *train de chiens* if you want to," she said turning toward me, "but I am not staying one second more. And I am going to complain to the railway company. *Alfred, descendons!*" [1]

There was a positively dog-like submission in the way Pochet obeyed Madame's injunction. The whole business seemed to have numbed him with stupefaction. And I shall remember all my life the sight of this man standing mesmerized on the platform as a train full of dogs pulled out before his eyes.

Like my two-legged fellow passengers, I resigned myself to standing for the better part of the night, and as the best places in the corridor were already taken, I was reduced to leaning up against the door of the W.C. in a

[1] Mme Pochet's complaint, together with those of several other passengers whose love of dogs was not unlimited, were duly registered with the offices of the British Railways, which issued a formal statement of policy a few days later: in general, a dog, even an English dog with his ticket, does not have the right to occupy a railway seat, but in this case the dogs were quite exceptional. The British Railways had, therefore, decided to treat them as gentlemen and had authorized them to occupy passenger seats and even whole compartments. "The only thing for which we can reproach certain owners is their not having put rugs on the seats before setting down their animals," an official declared.

posture that reminded me of train trips during the German occupation of France.

As I was trying to doze off in this position under the mocking gaze of a cocker spaniel, who with drooping tongue was jeering at me from the elevation of his corner seat, I wondered if I weren't the victim of a hallucination. I used to imagine that in the infinite diversity of the planets there must exist one on which man was the noblest conquest of the horse. But it had never occurred to me that to find this kind of world it was unnecessary to cross the Milky Way; it was enough to cross the Channel. No, I was not dreaming; that night I was in the United Dogdom. The Pochets had indeed got off this British train and left me to roll on alone toward York. And if, at that very moment, a Saint Bernard conductor had suddenly appeared to punch my ticket with his teeth, I would not have been unduly surprised.

This strange sensation grew stronger in me when, unable to sleep upright, I pulled out the paper and started to read.

In normal times it is pretty hard to open a British paper without reading that Welsh miners are going on strike to get a forty-hour week for their ponies (one and a half columns), or that one of the Queen's three corgies bit a guard at Buckingham Palace, who didn't budge one

"I know. It's a bit awkward, but the General asked if he could bring along his best friend."

millimeter (two columns and a photo). But this evening the paper beat all records.

Whereas only four lines were needed to bury Lord Ramsay Featherspin, three entire columns (with photo) were devoted to the life of Black Knight, the well-known

Pekinese, who had just died in "his country house in Essex at the age of nine years and nine months." Imagine opening a French paper and finding five lines on the death of Paul Claudel and, in the same issue, a full half-page on the glorious career of Mme Pochet's poodle—and you'll have some idea of the situation!

But here's the point: are there in France dogs like Black Knight? Dogs that sit at the Lord Mayor's table on black satin cushions, eat off the gold plate at the Guildhall, and become honorary citizens of the City of London? Dogs that attend Queen Elizabeth's wedding in sable coats, have an entrée to Buckingham Palace, have their own club, make telephone calls to Naples, profess political opinions, and pay calls on the Prime Minister at 10 Downing Street?[2] Dogs that write their autobiographies and

\wwwwwwwwwwwwww

[2] The members of the Kennel Club in London, which is reserved for owners of eminent hounds, are veritable man-dogs and woman-dogs. They are addressed not by their own names, but by those of their pedigreed beasts. "Hello, Black!" "How are you, Husky?" The presentation of new members is likewise made in the names of their dogs.

As for telephone calls to Naples, reference is here made to those which an English actress, Elizabeth Reber, carries on from Capri with Patch, her Queensland Blue Heeler, who receives the communication comfortably seated in his armchair at Grosvenor Cottage, Sloane Square, London. Miss Reber speaks and Patch barks, Miss Reber's mother hold-open bank accounts of £50,000 with their royalties? [3]

Obviously not. And in the circumstances it is easy enough to understand how Lady Mennings, Black Knight's companion—one can hardly use the word "proprietor," for if anyone was possessed in this affair, it was clearly not the dog—should say of him after his death:

"He was the incarnation of a Chinese Emperor and a Ming horse. I am inconsolable. But I shall send him to the taxidermist and when Black Knight comes back stuffed, he can sleep forever in his favorite spot—on my bed, his head on his paws."

Still leaning against the door, I finally fell asleep that night. My fitful slumbers were only briefly disturbed every half-hour or so when some bulldog or Great Dane would tread nicely over me to get to the lavatory. At last I understood the full meaning of the remark made to me by an Italian mason in Arlington Street at the sight of a

〰〰〰〰〰〰〰〰

ing the receiver for him. "It cheers me up when I'm feeling blue!" Miss Reber declared to a group of somewhat startled Neapolitan journalists.

In the same way many Conservatives and Socialists see to it that their dogs have the same political opinions as they themselves. With a little training a Socialist poodle can be made to refuse sugar offered in the name of Churchill and accept it in the name of Gaitskell.

[3] Black Knight's autobiography was published in England under the title *The Diary of a Freeman.*

9 3

chauffeur opening the door of a Bentley for a Pekinese dressed in a sealskin: *"Se dovessi vivere ancora una volta, vorrei essere un cane in Inghilterra"* ("If I had to live a second time, I would like to be a dog in England").

Toward one o'clock in the morning I was awakened by a sharp pain in the stomach, and I resumed my reading of the paper. My eye was caught by an advertisement which, by a happy coincidence, applied exactly to my case: "Are you suffering from gastric pains? Do you feel depressed? Take some AZOTYME."

I immediately wrote down the name of the panacea. But when I asked the chemist at York the next morning how to imbibe the medicine, he looked at me with astonished eyes. The advertisement that I had noticed was addressed to the dog population of Great Britain—to greyhounds, bulldogs, and fox terriers. All animals of my species were excluded.[4]

~~~~~~~~~~~~~~~~~~~~~

[4] Advertisements in English newspapers are directed at dogs, cats, and horses (their respective communities being always referred to as "populations") as much as at men. "Can you go out on a day like this?" runs the spattered streamer of a poster that in France would advertise a woman's raincoat. But here it is a cat, his tail raised like a question mark, which asks the question from behind a pane of glass. And it's another cat that answers him: "Yes . . . because I use TIBS. So take some TIBS, my dear; you will feel completely refreshed. *Tibs, a vitaminized product, makes cats frisky.*"

Even when advertising beer, whisky, or soap, the leading firms

Snow was falling in great flakes when I reached Pickhill, near York, the country house of Colonel Basil Cranborne, where the Major was expecting me.

"My dear Daninos, your breakfast awaits you in the dining-room," Marmaduke shouted at me from the top of the stairs. "Basil's gone off to the vet, I'm almost through my shave, and I'll be with you in a jiffy!"

While waiting for the Major, I listened to the latest news on the radio. An unusually heavy snowstorm had blanketed the British Isles during the night. In many places villages were isolated and human lives endangered. This announcement was followed by some political news. Then, after a moment of silence, one of those beautifully modulated, sober, and distinguished voices—the trademark of the BBC announcer—made the following appeal:

"Do not forget that the snow keeps the little birds from finding their food. So put out little bits of bread, bacon, and cake crumbs in your gardens. Put out bowls of water. Please think of the little birds!"

There was another moment of silence, during which

------

make their appeal to the (human) public through the medium of seals, penguins, or kangaroos. Nothing like them to attract the eye of an Englishman! If a Technicolor film star asserts that such-and-such a cold cream is marvelous, that's fine; but if a walrus gives his solemn word, that's even better.

I expected to hear an appeal on behalf of the homeless—
a habit derived, no doubt, from listening to the Abbé
Pierre. Instead, it was jazz music that now came on—and
stayed.[5]

"Hello, old boy!" Major Thompson cried, when he
finally came down. "Well, and how was your trip? But
where in heaven's name are the Pochets?"

When I told Marmaduke of our separation, his
hearty laugh boomed through the quiet dining-room. The
Major agreed that the railway had gone a little too far,
but "after all, they were very valuable dogs." I advised
him not to hazard any observations of this kind to Mme
Pochet the next time he saw her.

"But, my dear fellow, we regard animals as superior

ᴧᴧᴧᴧᴧᴧᴧᴧᴧᴧᴧᴧᴧᴧᴧᴧᴧ

[5] It would seem that the British radio and television closely follow
the wishes of at least one reader of the TV *Mirror* who wrote in a letter:
"I suggest that the BBC introduce a program from 7:00 to 7:25 a.m.
entitled, 'Pussies' Half-Hour,' during which we would hear nothing but
animal voices, and above all bird songs. I am convinced that such a
broadcast would greatly help to pacify our dogs and cats, who are so
often sad or nervous when we are busy with television."

Paul Morand, that fine connoisseur of the English animal, relates
that when he was on the staff of the French Embassy in London, every
spring the Embassy would get a note from the Foreign Office begging
the French Government to take all possible measures to ensure that the
little migratory birds returning from North Africa to the north would not
be shot down by the inhabitants of southern France.

beings for the very reason that makes you treat them as inferiors. They don't possess that wretched thing which makes us commit so many idiocies—speech. How could we who employ such circumlocutions to avoid stating the bald truth not feel an unbounded admiration for beings who never say anything at all? No matter how hard he tries, the most tongue-tied Englishman will always remain inferior to a dog, because sooner or later in his life he will be forced to say: "How do you do?" [6]

"Is that," I asked, "a reason for showing more tenderness to a dog than to a child? One of your masters can break his cane on the back of a public-school boy, and no one will say a word of protest. But if I break the leg of a dog that has bitten me, I may end up in prison."

"Well, you'd at least have the whole neighborhood, not to say the whole country, against you. For there's only a *National* Society for the protection of the young, whereas there's a *Royal* Society for the protection of animals. The difference is significant."

"And you find this normal? A psychoanalyst . . ."

"You and your logic! Next thing and you'll be pull-

〰〰〰〰〰〰〰〰

[6] This is certainly the opinion of a Justice of the High Court who exclaimed in the course of a recent trial: "If there are no dogs in heaven, I don't want to go there!"

ing out that old chestnut about frustration: 'The tenderness we refuse our children we lavish on our Pekinese.'
There's some truth in all that, but a lot of nonsense, too. I
won't deny that we think it less ridiculous to stroke a cat
than to pamper a small boy. We bring up our boys severely
because one day they must become men; we pet a dog because it will always remain a child. Besides, we don't
really pamper him; we simply play with him. We love
playing. We adore dogs because you can play with them
right up to the day they die. Take Colonel Cranborne, for
example. His wife has got the flu, and he's gone to see the
vet."

"You mean that he is having her treated like a
horse?"

"Certainly not! But he's in a far greater rush to get
someone to look at his old Newfoundland, who is stretched
out in the warmest and most comfortable room in the
house, than he is to fetch a doctor to look at the boring
old flu of his wife, who is asleep in an icy bedroom. But
that doesn't keep us from being a lot more sentimental
than you think. Look at the way all Britain from the Ork-
neys to Guernsey can be worked up over the happiness of
the Princess—at the idea that she can't marry her heart's
desire. Or take that forbidding Jennifer, whose heart, you
think, is made of stone because of the way she maintains

"*James, put on another cat, I feel a bit of a draft.*"

that Spartan discipline so dear to Mrs. Cripplestone. Do you know what her first thought is of a winter morn when it's bitter cold and she's shivering under her ratteen coat? 'Let's hope the Queen's well covered!' Most of the time we hide this sentimentality beneath a chilly shell. It's what you so stupidly label 'hypocrisy,' that word which you use as a sort of master key for unlocking us. At least we act this way only with our equals. But with animals the barriers are lifted, and we can give free rein to our feelings."

"Your admiration for animals does not keep you from stalking foxes. . . ."

"Rubbish! We never shoot them! It's a contest between them and the hounds. But how can you understand the intoxication that seizes an Englishman when of an autumn day he hurls his horse across the countryside, jumping stream and bush, fence and hedge, in full pursuit of a fox? He draws all England into his lungs. And everyone is happy—horses, hounds, men."

"And the fox, too, I suppose?"

"Yes, even the fox. He enjoys the sport. He plays. . . . It's only the last minute or so that can be a bit nasty for him. Too bad! But where's the cruelty in all this? The really cruel thing would be to deprive those stout dogs of a meal after they've run a hundred miles."

The Major always knows the answer.

"Give me Italy, please."

That Major Thompson's countrymen should be more concerned with the fate of animals than of men was borne in
on me in striking fashion the very day I landed in England.
The catastrophe at Orléansville had just aroused a world-
wide wave of sympathy, and I was, therefore, not surprised to see on the front page of *The Times* a little announcement, headlined:

EARTHQUAKE IN ALGERIA

SEND CONTRIBUTIONS IMMEDIATELY

But it was to the Royal Society for the Prevention of
Cruelty to Animals that these donations were to be sent,
for as a result of the earthquake thousands of mules,

horses, cats, and dogs had been made homeless. Of human victims, there was not a word.

Several days later I attended a session of the House of Commons with Major Thompson. Facing each other across the floor in front of the bewigged Speaker, MP's from both sides of the House were engaged in a bitter battle of words in that traditional parliamentary style which allows one man to call another a fool as long as he prefaces it with the word "Honourable."

"What," I asked the Major, "is the subject of this violent debate? The atomic bomb, nationalized industry?"

"Myxomatosis, my dear fellow."

What was at issue was not the danger of contamination, since myxomatosis is not transmissible to man (besides which, no Englishman worthy of the name eats rabbit), but the peril that this scourge represented for English cats, whose favorite dish is rabbit. The Honourable Members were doubly aroused because of a dockers' strike that had halted the unloading of merchandise in British ports. No one was worried by the thought of starving. The uproar was due to the fact that the strike had stopped delivery of frozen meat from Australia, the only suitable food for English cats since the outbreak of the myxomatosis epidemic in Europe.

It so happened that the next question on the agenda

was poliomyelitis. Instantly passions subsided. Several MP's went out to have a cup of tea, and the problem was dealt with in an atmosphere of general indifference.[7]

"If animals had a pope," Major Thompson said to me, "their Vatican would be in London. And if by some dire submarine cataclysm that noble vessel Great Britain were to be shipwrecked and start to founder, believe me, there would surely be somebody in Westminster to cry from the top of the Tower: 'Dogs first!' "[8]

〰〰〰〰〰〰〰

[7] I am not inventing this, unfortunately. I refer the conscientious reader to the *Daily Telegraph* of the 27th of December, 1954, which emphasized the contrast between the heated nature of this debate and the dullness of the one that followed.

[8] I could go on endlessly citing examples to prove that the English harbor a secret sympathy for the cat-o'-nine-tails when it comes to men, while lavishing bucketfuls of tenderness on animals, even of the most monstrous sort. One night I was in a Piccadilly theater watching a documentary film on underwater fishing in the Mediterranean. The film showed an Italian frogman being seized by the tentacles of a giant octopus, from which he managed to free himself only after the most dramatic struggle. He finally succeeded in running his harpoon through the body of the monster, whose black blood darkened the sea. The lady sitting next to me, who had not shown the slightest feeling for the diver, could not, on seeing the octopus mortally wounded, keep herself from clutching her neighbor's arm and murmuring: "Poor little thing!"

Even when they are their hapless victims, the English can't bring themselves to complain of the behavior of animals. Never for a moment did it occur to them to kill the gorilla in the London zoo which tore off the arms and caused the hideous death of an over-bold child. Of a less serious nature was the bite that the dog of a celebrated actor, A. E. Matthews, took out of his master's lip, but it was still serious enough to keep him off the sets. Attempts were made to stifle the truth, and the first communiqué announced that the film star was suffering from lung trouble. The actor, however, changed his mind: "I wanted to conceal what actually happened, for Charlie (a four-year-old Kerry Blue) is heartbroken over what he did. The truth is I asked him to kiss me, but he was a bit too passionate." (It cost him two stitches and he was out of commission for a week.)

Chapter 7

FACTORIES FOR GENTLEMEN

The English, who tenderly employ the feminine for their battleships, leave their children in the neuter. In a land where it is often easier to determine the gender of a man-of-war than of a man of the world and where the number of sexes is definitely greater than two, this neuter is at once prudent and significant.

This is not to say, of course, that the English are lacking in affection for their children because they don't pamper them like their dogs or deck them out like their yachts. Their peculiar way of displaying attachment is by detachment—by severing themselves from their children and having them brought up by specialists. This may seem odd, but in a realm where the animal is king, what greater homage could a Briton pay his children than to have them brought up like horses?

Not unlike those owners who to have them compete in the Derby must sign up their colts at birth, the English enter their newborn progeny in the registers of those venerable gentleman stud farms: Eton, Harrow, and Winchester. Here their sons learn far more about jumping hedges, being flogged, running steeplechases, and curbing their instincts than about becoming, like the Latins, thinking reeds. These public schools, as the name implies, are private institutions where one pays dearly for the privilege of being beaten, as opposed to the state schools, which are public institutions where one pays nothing to escape corporal punishment. Their purpose is not so much to sharpen wits as to forge characters.

I was with Major Thompson one fine spring morning when he was trying to explain all this to his wife, Martine. We were looking over Eton as a possible choice for Nicholas's schooling. Through the quiet streets of the old town ruddy-cheeked boys in black tail coats were sauntering along, their hands in their pockets. On meeting a master in his black gown, a boy would take one hand out of his pocket and salute with a negligent forefinger, the master responding, according to tradition, with an even more nonchalant index. The boys who were not in tails wore striped blazers, gray flannel shorts, and caps, and were bound for the playing fields, armed with cricket bats and oars. Through the tall lancet-windows of a neo-Gothic hall we could see three boys taking a 1929 Rolls to pieces (Practical Works). Aside from that, at three o'clock on this Monday afternoon, the classrooms were empty.

"So this is what you call education, *mon Marminet!*" Martine exclaimed, an evident note of irony in her voice.

The Major, who seemed elated to find himself once again in the familiar haunt of his youth, gazed up at the sky for a moment and then said: "It would be interesting to know if God created spring afternoons for the young to find square roots in dusty classrooms or to play cricket on the open sward. Martine, dear, when I think that the Almighty can at one and the same instant behold the young girls of Wycombe Abbey issuing from their houses to play lacrosse and those of the Lycée Victor Duruy in Paris closeting themselves indoors to calculate the surface area of the cone, I think I can guess which way His heart inclines. . . . Your young children at the end of a school year look like ailing septuagenarians, whereas our old-timers have the rosy cheeks of college boys. In France, really, you don't do enough sports!"

"In England you do too much . . . and because you do, you produce *des imbéciles!*"

"Ridiculous!" spluttered the Major. "Another of your absurd prejudices against British education! Meredith noted, and I'm convinced he was right, that there are about as many fools in England as in France. But an English fool is a fool pure and simple, whereas a French fool is a fool who reasons.[1] The English are sometimes ignorant, but their strength is in not knowing it. That's a damned sight better than being highly intelligent and over-aware of one's weaknesses. Hitler had 200 divisions at his command and the continent of Europe under his boot while the gentlemen of the City were still doing the manual of arms with their umbrellas in the streets of London. Any reasoning animal could have recognized the inevitability of their defeat. But there wasn't a Briton worthy of the name who entertained the notion for an instant."

Martine grew thoughtful for a moment.

"All right," she said, "but, in any case, I do not want Nicholas to be caned . . . any more than I could

〰〰〰〰〰〰〰〰

[1] The Major himself didn't hesitate to say one day about the members of the Cavalry Club: "Some officers are so dense that even their fellow officers notice it."

bear to have you follow the matrimonial advice of the Reverend Father McCaskill by giving me a spanking every now and then."

Martine, it should be said, had been deeply stirred that same morning by several things she had read in the *Daily Express*. The first was an article expounding the theory of conjugal bliss of the Reverend McCaskill, a Presbyterian minister. ("From time to time it is a good thing for young couples to inflict punishment on each other. Certain complexes won't stand up long under a spanking.") The second was a dispatch appearing under the bold headline:

THE HEAD CANES
200 BOYS

The story that followed told how Mr. Oliver Whitfield, the headmaster of Usworth School, had failed to discover the author of an obscene drawing that had appeared on the school entrance. Whereupon he had decided to mete out an assembly-line punishment: 200 whacks administered to 200 outstretched hands. The London dailies had immediately sent their reporters to get the details of the story—not from the boys, but from the headmaster. The headmaster, worn out by an arduous day, was resting, so his wife undertook to answer their questions.

"Of course, Oliver's arm aches, but you can say, at any rate, that he would have done the same thing with his own children."

When the victims were interviewed in their turn, they displayed not the slightest bitterness, but rather a certain admiration for the athletic prowess of their headmaster. "This Mr. Whitfield is really tough," said a fourteen-year-old student. "He kept up the same pace for twenty-five minutes non-stop. Mine was the two hundredth hand, and I can assure you that the last blow was as hard as the first."

"Altogether an exceptional case," said the Major, somewhat put out. "The proof of it is that the newspapers reported it."

"Well," said Martine stubbornly, "I do not want my son beaten, even *exceptionnellement,* by someone I do not know."

"Then he'll never be a real gentleman."

"I do not see the connection."

"You'll never understand the first thing about us, my dear. It's Eton, Harrow, and Winchester that produce our leaders. And what is the first duty of a leader? Self-control. And what is the first thing one must learn in order to control oneself? To be controlled by somebody else." [2]

[2] London still boasts a Society for the Propagation of Corporal Punishment, and manuals on *The Whip through the Ages* are still prominently displayed in the windows of orthopedic shops around Charing Cross. It must be said, however, that corporal punishment is much less frequent now in the public schools. It remains a standard penalty only for serious misdemeanors. The headmaster undertakes the beating personally, or else authorizes another to do so for him. The students themselves are the first to defend the system. A teacher at a London school recently asked his pupils whether they preferred being retained in class after hours or being caned, and a crushing majority came out for corporal punishment on the grounds that it is over more quickly and affords an opportunity for displaying courage. When a woman journalist named Anne Scott-James dared to stigmatize these "Spartan methods" in the *Sunday Express,* she was met with an avalanche of protests. A thirteen-year-old schoolboy wrote her: "When I read your article to my schoolmates, they burst into howls of laughter. Would you like each of us to have his own little Teddy Bear? Everything you say is utter nonsense. We are all very happy."

According to the statistics collected by Geoffrey Gorer, the author of some remarkable studies of British behavior, most English parents are in favor of corporal punishment. Some of them even display in their enthusiasm refinements that Freud would have delighted in. A father of three children approved of wholesale punishment for both sexes, recommending "spanking in the presence of other children to humble the self-esteem of the wrongdoer." A fifty-seven-year-old father in Wolverhampton suggested that naughty boys should be dressed up in little girls' clothes. Gorer ran into such a variety of corporal punishments that he thought it a good idea to draw up a synoptic chart showing the relative penchant of fathers and mothers for this or that specialty: (a) caning, (b) thrashing, (c) punching, (d) birching, (e) flogging.

In learning to control himself, the young Englishman can rely as much on the student prefects as on his masters. Nothing could be better for a future lord or for a governor-to-be, destined one day to rule the peoples of Bechuanaland and Uganda, than to begin his career as the slave of a sixteen-year-old boy who can call on him, as a "fag," to make his toast, to brush his topper, to carry messages on the double to another prefect, and to polish the floor. Public-school education seems to have been designed to prepare every boy eventually to become Viceroy of India. There is no India any more, but the old methods remain. During the period of his life when he is reduced to servitude, the future gentleman may well emit an unfavorable judgment on the public schools. But, first, he is not asked for his opinion, and he would look ridiculous were he to give it. Second, and above all, he waits with confidence for his hour of revenge—when it's his turn to bully. Never would it occur to an Etonian or a Harrovian to write a sobbing letter home telling of the caning he just received. He would lose face for life before his family, his fellows, and himself. A real gentleman never complains. He must know how to take it.[3] Canings, freezing dormitories,

wwwwwwwwwwwwwww

[3] A French doctor—Dr. Lugnier, of Marcilly-sur-Seine (Marne)— recently wrote me of the following incident, which he witnessed in De-

"And now, we Old Boys will show you lads what we used to have to take when we were at school."

rationing—the Englishman accepts everything without grumbling, and the moment some regulation, as a matter of national necessity, forbids him to eat more than 8 ounces of meat a week, he would not dream of eating 8.1 ounces. It wouldn't be cricket.

Does this mean that these people don't enjoy good food, hot water, or cosy beds? No. But they enjoy even more, perhaps, showing the world that they can do without them.[4]

Whenever an indignant mother or an overzealous reformer launches a campaign in favor of the abolition of corporal punishment, *The Times* receives a flood of letters from aged gentlemen who proudly recall the times when they were beaten. A septuagenarian will write: "I shall remember to my dying day the time I was beaten because, as a first-year man at Harrow, I had buttoned only two, instead of three, of my coat buttons. It was a lesson I am

~~~~~~~~~~~~~~~~

cember of 1955. "A young couple (French wife, English husband) suddenly lost an eight-month-old child (neurotoxicosis, dead in 48 hours). Gathered around the cot, the French family shed warm tears. The husband's mother arrived—typically English mien. The French sobbing was redoubled. "You are crying?" the English woman asked the mother of the young woman. "You mean you don't cry?" the other replied. "We cry," said the impassive English woman, "but at night."

[4] The more famous a school, the more uncomfortable it is.

proud to have received." At a ceremony at Haileybury College, Mr. Attlee himself recalled with some pride how he had been one of eighty-two boys who had received a caning in 1900 as a result of a student demonstration.

An Englishman's first dominion is the one he must maintain over himself. Be master of oneself to be master of the world—such is the spirit in which the boys are brought up at public schools, whose first aim is the manufacture of gentlemen. But it would be a mistake to think that only the public schools, reserved as they are for the sons of the well-to-do and a few recipients of scholarships, go in for this kind of manufacture. The humblest English schools share the same ambition and their students model their manners on those taught at the great colleges. In this land where the workingman copies the lower-middle-class man, who copies the upper-middle-class man, who imitates the aristocracy, which takes its cue from the sovereign, who shakes hands with the workingman—everyone aspires to "gentlemanize" himself.

But just what is a gentleman?

To the French, a gentleman is someone who kisses a lady's hand and yields his seat to a woman in the subway. But this summary notion has little to do with the idea of a gentleman in England, where ladies' hands are never kissed and where a man who wants to give up his seat risks being put in his place by a woman who feels she resents such a mark of condescension.

The definition of the perfect gentleman was enunciated back in 1440 in the statutes of All Souls College at Oxford, the highest university authority in the realm: *"Bene nati, bene vestiti, et mediocriter docti"* ("Well born, well dressed, and moderately learned").

This definition remains essentially valid in a country where intelligence is considered an insidious disease that only discretion can palliate. It is, however, inexact as regards clothing. To a farmer, a gentleman is somebody who on Sunday can allow himself to don a pair of patched-up trousers with a tie around his waist for a belt. To a workingman, a gentleman is somebody who pronounces the *h* and wears a bowler hat on weekdays.[5] To a gentleman, a

[5] Summary but not inaccurate. If I could do it, or, rather, if he could reach it himself, I would have Daninos crash that "sound barrier" so audible to the aristocratic ear which allows us, by sole virtue of an *h* or an *o*, to determine the social origins of an individual. It would be a jolly good thing, in this connection, to undertake a geological survey of English society, beginning with the Foreign Office crust, the bowler stratum, and the neolithic substratum of mustachioed Majors in retirement. But suffice it to say, for the moment and until I can find the time to devote myself to these new excavations, that with us the stratification of classes is such that it applies even to dogs. A publicity folder for a hotel in the seaside resort of Torquay says: "Dogs are charged for at the rate of 1s. 6d. to 3s., according to the size and social standing of the dog." (W.M.T.)

gentleman—someone who dies without ever pronouncing the word—is a man who climbs Everest, never mentions it to a soul, and listens politely to Pochet's account of how in 1937, in spite of his sciatica, he conquered the Puy de Dôme.° In a drawing-room a gentleman must, above all, avoid talking about that which he knows best. Heaven forbid that he be taken for one of those experts or professionals whom the English, those sturdy champions of the amateur, so abhor. An Englishman who wishes to be a physician must work hard to become a "Doctor"; but he must work even harder to rebecome a "Mister." Once he is a surgeon, he considers it a great privilege to be called "Mister" again like everyone else.

These ways of speaking, dressing, and behaving, of treating war as sport and sport as war, are contracted, like some healthy malady, by the gentleman-to-be first at the public school and then at the university. For manners are not so much learned as transmitted—by contagion.

Torn at the tenderest age from the bosom of the family,[7] the English child is placed in one of those medieval

vvvvvvvvvvvvvvvvvvv

° A 4,500-foot hump in Central France. (W.M.T.)

[7] It would appear that English children take their revenge on their parents when they grow up. Heartlessly banished to freezing dormitories and canings, the young later get even with their elders by packing them off to grim boardinghouses, like Mrs. Cripplestone's, where, solitary and

nurseries called public schools to suck the milkbottle of tradition. There is just one way of wearing a straw hat at Harrow, of saluting the masters at Eton, of walking (in groups) for the young girls at Wycombe Abbey, and of carrying books and notebooks at Charterhouse. There is just one way, everywhere, of sleeping and working, winter and summer, rain or shine—and that is with the windows wide open. What does it matter if the way is good or bad? It is the one that was adopted 300 or 600 years ago, and that is all that matters. What does it matter if studies are less important than sports? The floor of the Alec Fitch Room, where the boys of Harrow take their first steps as gentlemen, is made from the oak of the ships of Trafalgar. The history of Napoleon can perfectly well come after cricket; it is absorbed by osmosis.[8]

wwwwwwwwwwwwwwww

abandoned, hundreds of thousands of aging English men and women eke out their days on a diet of cabbage soup.

[8] The history of England is, of course, accorded top place in the minds of English public-school boys. I realized to what extent this was true one day when I attended a history class at Harrow. The master, Mr. Herbert Harris, kindly let me ask some questions of his students (fourteen and fifteen years old). I asked them which French king had been guillotined. "Louis XI," said the first. "Louis XII," said the second. The sixth got the answer right, and Mr. Harris called the game off. I then asked them who had burned Joan of Arc, and they all replied in a chorus: "The French." We took leave of each other on good terms. All these boys looked healthy, happy, and friendly. Out of twenty boys, only six had been beaten.

On benches where Peel and Gladstone have carved their names, the young boy grows up convinced that all that is best in the world is British—ships as well as woolens, secret services as well as zoos, butlers as well as airplanes. Take the climate. The children of Albion are taught that England is an ideal country with a temperate climate; the inhabitants seem to be the only ones who know it.[9]

In the shadow of tall brick walls and on the green carpets of century-old lawns, the young Englishman is marked with an imprint that nothing will efface. When for seven long years you have become used to living with 800 boys, to making the same gestures, observing the same rites, putting on the same clothes, obeying the same rules, and practicing the same sports in the same team spirit, you bear an indelible stamp. No matter what career he chooses, the Englishman throughout his life carries on him the hallmark of his college, and he seizes the slightest opportunity to re-immerse himself in its beneficent waters. If you have seen with what joy the Bishop of Willesden abandons his cross and his miter and dons his Old School

wwwwwwwwwwww

[9] Only with regard to music are the English prone to be more modest. Speaking of the Albert Hall, renowned for its acoustics, Sir Thomas Beecham once said: "It's the only place in the world where English composers stand a chance of having their works played twice."

cap and white ducks in order to go out on the Thames to umpire the Oxford-Cambridge boat race, then you will understand that the English are born gentlemen and die children. The septuagenarian who proudly writes to *The Times* about his first caning is not an old man; he's an Old Boy.

Beneath the prelate, beneath the statesman, the college boy is ever visible. Both apply to the affairs of the world the solid principles of cricket, club, and college. When Churchill said to Stalin that to be a member of the "Great Powers Club" one had to have an entrance qualification of four million soldiers, it was Harrow speaking to Yalta. It was a septuagenarian super-prefect, wrapped in his gown of tradition and privilege, laying down a new Marquis of Queensberry rule. When former Home Secretary David Lloyd George spoke of a possible settlement with the Russians and the Chinese, he began by inviting these people to play cricket—it would simplify everything. And when Mrs. Cripplestone wanted to explain Hitler to me, she said: "The trouble with that man Hitler is that he never went to a really good school."

Chapter 8

[P.D.]

BIBLE, BRIDE, AND BRITON

"To open up an Englishman," Major Thompson once said to me, "there are two master keys: whisky and the Bible."

As I don't always walk around with a Bible on me (or with a bottle of whisky, for that matter), many Englishmen remain closed books to me. But one day while reading the Sunday paper I realized just how right the Major was. British Sunday papers are very important for the proper understanding of the English. Here you can read everything, and in the greatest detail, that the English dare not say out loud (the things the French will say, but wouldn't dare write). And in this way, along with some 20 million fellow readers, you can easily scale the supposedly inviolable walls surrounding Mr. Smith's private life.

In this particular case Mr. Smith was called Mr. Jones, and he was suing his wife for divorce. Mr. Jones, it seems was a cuckold. In France this type of person inspires the writers of comedies, but in England he inspires sympathy. What had happened was that Mr. Jones had undertaken to read his wife the fifty-first Psalm—the one in which David repents of having committed adultery with Bathsheba. This was too much for his wife, who, afflicted by a bad conscience and a good memory, thereupon confessed to having deceived him thirty years before. And as though this blow weren't enough, she went on to inform him that his son, Eric, was not his own. Mr. Jones, in truth, might well have suspected as much, for the fact was that, to use the legal formula, he had never "consummated." His leisure evening hours had always been almost exclusively devoted to reading the Bible in the company of his wife. Fervent Baptists, both of them, they attended public readings of the Scriptures every evening at the Parish House of Bermondsey.

This tranquil state of affairs had been interrupted thirty years before by the appearance on the scene of William Henry West, an equally faithful member of the Band of Hope. These healthy evening distractions evidently

failed to satisfy Mr. West, for one day, returning home unexpectedly (normal husbands return home at normal
hours, but deceived husbands always come home at impossible hours), Mr. Jones found Mr. West with his wife.
The least that can be said is that they were not reading the
Bible, though they were literally applying the basic com-
mandment: Love ye one another.

Whether it was through greatness of soul or some
other motive, the fact remains that Mr. Jones did not pro-
voke a row. He simply remarked to Mr. West that in his
estimation he had no business behaving this way with his
wife. Some time later, as she was accompanying her husband to the train at St. Pancras (English trains themselves
never stray too far from the Scriptures) which was to take
him to Manchester, Mrs. Jones told him that she was preg-
nant. As Mr. Jones had made no attempt on her for the
past five years, this appeared a bit odd to him, but the
train's departure interrupted the course of his reflections.
When he returned home, his wife, who had gathered together a formidable mass of documentation, persuaded
him that one can have children without what the English
so poetically described as "sexual intercourse."

Mr. Jones consequently raised no objection to recog-
nizing Eric as his son. Most of the Bermondsey parishion-
ers remember a man who was very happy the day the

child was born. He must have been a little less so when rumors began to reach him that Eric was not his son. Still, as a worthy citizen of the land of *wait and see,* he had to wait some twenty-five years before his reading of the Scriptures elicited a frank explanation from his wife. He then decided to sue for divorce, laying the blame on his wife and her co-respondent (a word used by the British to designate a lover and which is, after all, not particularly shocking in a country where the vocabulary of love owes more to the Chamber of Commerce than to the *Kâmasûtra,* and where a *liaison* is called an "affair").

The judge, however, refused to accept Mr. Jones's claims and even sentenced him to pay the cost of the trial, including travel expenses for the lover. As for Mrs. Jones, she stayed at home, and there that very same evening Mr. Jones found her—this time alone and once again ready to read the Bible.[1]

~~~~~~~~~~~~~~~~~~~~

[1] This story clearly shows the Bible's importance in the daily life of the British. They find everything in it: consolation, hope, explanation, recreation. It quite often happens that in the midst of naval maneuvers (between two rival commands) an Admiral and a Vice-Admiral will exchange messages by semaphore quoting passages from the Gospel according to St. Matthew. It would be quite a job to count up the number of English societies whose only function is the distribution of the Bible. There is even one, with headquarters in London, known as *The Society for Distributing the Holy Scriptures to the Jews.* It is well nigh impossible

to spend a day in England without coming into direct or indirect contact with the Bible—even if only through small newspaper announcements containing celestial messages or quotations from the Authorized Version of 1611. Considering the Good Lord and the Saints to be subscribers to *The Times,* many practicing English men and women whose wishes have been fulfilled choose this way of bringing their thanks to the attention of Heaven, with such two-line messages as: "To Saint George with the expression of my gratitude and thanks. J.N.W."

Chapter 9

MARTINE AND THE ENGLISH

I think it's high time I took up the pen again to set matters straight. This Jones story, singular as it may be, has occurred more than once in England, I'll grant you, but it shouldn't lead anyone to believe that we British never "consummate." There's nothing I distrust more than this French mania for generalization.

Come what may, the English will always look upon the French as frivolous, sex-obsessed people. The French, for their part, will always regard the English as iceboxes, persuaded as they have been, ever since Stendhal, that we feel an urge once a fortnight and grow stiff with *ennui* while waiting out the intervals.

Ennui—always that confounded word!

Anyone who has watched a real honest-to-goodness Englishman snoozing in his club or dozing through a cricket match will have to admit that the Englishman savors his boredom as much as the Frenchman does his little game of *belote* in the *café*. The only thing that really bores an Englishman is having somebody come along and bore him while he is happily boring himself. For there's nothing he enjoys more than relaxing in a state of complete vacuity. At such moments his mind is a vacant lot, and the last thing he wants for it is a tenant.

But how in the devil will I ever get this into Daninos's head? Or how, for that matter, can I make Martine realize, when she sees my old friend Arthur Palethorpe sitting alone on his shooting-stick in the middle of his Killmarnok woods, that far from being bored, he is engaged in his favorite pastime—bird-watching? The game I enjoy most in the world—cricket—bores Martine to distraction. *"Je trouve ça d'un long!"* she says. Well, I'll admit that a match can sometimes be a bit long and drawn out and that it may go on for five days (there was even, I recall, one memorable engagement in South Africa which lasted a whole week without really ending, the British team having to go home before it was over). But what of it? When I see a good bowler put on a devilish leg stump spin, it positively makes my spine tingle.

So I should be awfully sorry to see this Jones business send Daninos off on a false scent. The truth is that our women were greatly changed by the war. A mighty tidal wave arose to sweep away the old conventions. The corset of Victorian prejudices split open. By allowing women to drive generals up to the firing-line (or not far from it), the war created a new species—the man-woman. Today women are all over us. You find them everywhere—in the buses, in Parliament, in the Police Force. . . . They even pursue us into our clubs, where they are now often admitted one day a week.[1] Some of them behave with more abandon than American women. The twentieth century will go down in history as having witnessed two great explosions, each of which, in its own way, brought new suffering to men: the explosion of the atomic bomb and the explosion of the English woman.

Pochet got an inkling of this one day when he saw a lovely London cover-girl called Gwendolyn kiss, full on the lips, a Frenchman she hadn't known an hour before.

"Mais alors . . . mon cher Major," Pochet said to me, "here you are with your stories about Lady Plunkett

----

[1] By the side door and for limited periods only. On the days they are admitted to the dining-room a kind of no man's land of empty tables separates them from the tables occupied solely by men—thereby limiting the effects of this promiscuity.

enveloping the legs of her grand piano in muslin and advising her daughter the night before her marriage to close her eyes and think of England. . . ."

"It's obvious, my dear fellow," I said to him, "that you'll never understand the first thing about us. It's because there have been and still are Lady Plunketts among us that you run into Gwendolyns. They make up the two faces of Britain—one of them severe and puritanical, the other libertine and brazen. We still have people who consider it bad form to speak of what lies between the neck and the knees. We still have colleges where flirting is considered ridiculous.[2] The aim, if not the effect, of British education is to put children to sleep without allowing them to dream. And yet every day in some part of England a Lady Chatterley throws a county into an uproar. And when the devil gets into an English woman, nothing stops her, not even the sacrosanct barrier of classes. Here, look at this."

I handed Pochet a copy of the newspaper. It contained a story about the heiress to one of the oldest fami-

[2] In certain Oxford Colleges undergraduates are divided into three categories: (1) those interested in neither men nor women; (2) those interested in men; (3) those interested in women. It was not so long ago that the Fellows lost their privileges as "Senior Members" on getting married.

lies in England Miss Susan Dykmore, the sister of the "Queen's Champion" (the bearer of the Royal Standard on coronation day), who had eloped with a stablegroom eighteen years her senior who could neither read nor write.

Now it would be just as dangerous for my friend Daninos to generalize in the opposite sense.[3] The English woman is becoming emancipated, to be sure. Formerly matters pertaining to sex were banned from conversation and virtually condemned by a strait-laced modesty. To-day people are much freer in their love-making, but they don't talk about it any more than before. At heart, our country hasn't changed. Here, as in Shakespeare's time, you can still write the most beautiful love sonnets. But it remains a man's country. And in this man's country, where

wwwwwwwwwwwww

[3] Was the Major perhaps afraid that I would bring up some embarrassing comparisons? It is curious to note that in an interview published by the *Daily Mirror* James Webb, the stablegroom, declared: "What drew us together most was our love of horses." Now, *twelve months earlier*, the Major had written in his *Notebooks* à propos of his first wife, Ursula: "It wasn't so much love that united us as a mutual passion for horses." The Major and his translator (myself) at that time received a number of letters from irate Englishmen. "You exaggerate," they said. "Our women like horses, no doubt; but not to the extent of resembling them or marrying out of love for these noble beasts!" This groom, who had not, for obvious reasons, read *The Notebooks of Major Thompson*, has thus refuted the Major's and my critics, I would say. How true it is of life that even with the best will in the world one can invent nothing! (P.D.)

everything is done for men, nothing delights a woman more than to be taken for a man. She dreams less of being adored than of being independent. Her latest conquest is the trouser—to such an extent, indeed, that it is sometimes difficult for a foreigner in certain public services to decide if he is dealing with a man, a woman, or both.

Yes, my dear Pochet . . . with us in England love does not flow through the air as it does in your gentle land of perdition. Walk around Paris in the springtime and you can feel currents of love all about you. A pretty woman going by is in permanent contact with a thousand eyes. Even the most satisfied husband looks at her with the eyes of a lover. But here there is none of that kind of silent complicity of persons and things which makes the atmosphere of Latin countries so propitious for sentimental adventure. When a Paris policeman gives a summons to a young lady motorist, he does not behave in quite the same way as when he deals with a man. He tempers the law with an indulgent complicity. When a salesman shows off a pair of gloves to a *Parisienne*, there is love in the way he sings their praises, in the way he has her try them on. The English, on the other hand, think of one thing at a time—the summons, the gloves, or love—never the three together. All your French country *auberges* look as though they were harboring clandestine lovers. The *patronne* is on your side.

"On vous comprend . . . on sait ce que c'est, allez . . . la vie est si courte." The *patronne* may well have three children herself and know that Monsieur is the father of a family, but youth is fleeting—particularly at the age of fifty. In England we have none of those inns with names such as "The Seven Capital Sins" or "The Forbidden Fruit" where all is allowed. The omnipresence of the Bible and the vigilant eye of the manageress, ever ready to pounce on illicit couples, are enough to give you that guilt complex which Pochet complained about.

And yet there is love in England. The love of animals. The love of flowers. The love of gardening. The love of sport. The love of the Navy. The love of the Royal Family. Everywhere there is love—it isn't just to be found in *l'amour.* In the British order of things love is an element that takes its place among others. It has to be stowed somewhere.[4]

This is not to say, once again, that Englishmen are unsentimental. But because their love goes primarily to

---

[4] To be exact, in seventh place, as far as the relations between men and women are concerned—if we are to trust the statistics drawn up by Geoffrey Gorer, who asked a cross-section of English womanhood the qualities they looked for and appreciated in a husband: understanding (33%); attentiveness (28%); sense of humor (24%). Love (14%) was sandwiched in between "generosity" (17%) and "tolerance" (13%). (P.D.)

*It is sometimes hard, in England, to know whether one is deal-
ing with a man, a woman, or both.*

the nation, sport, and animals, the English woman has to take what is left. Most of our authors have held women in pretty low esteem—even our feminine authors. "I have never had any great esteem for the generality of the fair sex, and my only consolation . . . has been the assurance it gave me of never being married to any one among them." [5]

One radiant April morning Martine and I were walking through Hyde Park. Blue and white nurses were out walking rosy, blond children. Riders were galloping under the leaves. A few cocker spaniels were frolicking on the grass. A sorrel ridden by a young Amazon suddenly shied, throwing his rider to the ground. Galloping on for fifty yards, he ran straight into a fence and rolled over. A hundred people promptly rushed toward the horse, but barely five toward the lady.

"*C'est bien ça!*" Martine exclaimed. "You can walk all nude around London and no one will pay attention to you—unless you are accompanied by a dog."

Martine will never get used to the Englishman's apparent indifference to women. Never will she understand why his eyes don't linger over her, above all when she goes out, as was the case that morning, in a Balenchy suit. In

---

[5] This celebrated *bon mot* by Lady Mary Wortley Montagu, which dates from 1723, was picked up seventy-three years later by Mme de Staël. I have no idea from whom Lady Mary Wortley Montagu got it.

France women dress as much for themselves as for others. The same coquettish spirit is seldom found among English women, who like to be at their ease in "sensible" shoes and who display in their way of dressing a taste for nature and bright colors rather than a concern about men. Against the grayness of the weather they react with torrents of green and red. To counter the rain they put sunlight in their mackintoshes. Little does it matter how they will appear to men, since nine times out of ten they won't appear to them at all.

Some time ago one of our journalists launched a campaign against the hideousness of the uniforms worn in certain of our boarding-schools where the young girls are condemned to wear black stockings, rough serge pinafore dresses, and floppy purple felt hats with green ribbons—or else red hoods lined with purple. The reporter received a raft of protesting letters, such as this typical one from an indignant mother: "Those uniforms are made to be worn, not looked at."

One day Mrs. Cripplestone undertook to explain all this to Martine, but far from convincing her, she left her pensive.

"Martine, dear," I said, "you seem sad. I don't like those clouds in your eyes."

"It's your country that is sad, *Marminet*. Your country has no eyes. I put on *un amour de tailleur* this morning, but no one looked at me."

Mrs. Cripplestone gave a soft chuckle.

"Tut, tut, my dear. When I was young and pretty—for such was once the case—I used to take the train from Wimbledon to London, and I had the impression I put everybody off. The men entrenched themselves behind ramparts of newspapers, the women cast disapproving glances at me, and the conductor never spoke to me. But now that I am inoffensive everyone is nice to me. The men no longer hide their faces, the women look at me kindly, and the conductor speaks to me. I feel much more comfortable."

And Mrs. Cripplestone with a vegetable garden on her head now moves gaily through life. She no longer even thinks of "defending herself." Why defend oneself in a land where no one attacks?

Mrs. Cripplestone's case left Martine more baffled than ever. Later I explained to her that this was by no means an isolated case. In the very *éclat* of an English girl's beauty there is often something provocative that bothers the girl more than it delights her, and rather than stress it she does her best to tone it down.

When I ask Martine: "How do you find Englishmen?" and she answers: "Darling, I do not find them," I'm neither surprised nor particularly shocked. After all, she did find *me,* and I don't see why she should try to find any others.

The trouble, however, is that here in England Martine—at least, this is what she claims—can no longer find even me.

"When you are in your own country, *Marminet,* you are no longer the same man. *On dirait que tu as peur d'avoir l'air d'aimer!"* [6]

Good lord! It's not so far from the truth. But how on earth could it be otherwise? Martine has difficulty enough getting used to my dashing out for the evening paper to see if our bowlers have taken any more wickets in the Australian Test Match, or to my putting on a blazer and shorts to join some Old Boys on the Thames. But in the presence of Lady Osborne she manages to get her full revenge by tweaking my mustache with her little finger or pinching my crimson cheek and asking: "Don't you think, Lady Osborne, that he looks like a big cat?" Certainly not in England. And how can I listen to myself being called *Marminet* in front of Lord Ratcliffe without feeling horribly be-

---

[6] If I were to translate this literally as, "One would say you are afraid of giving the impression of loving," Daninos would probably hold it up as a proof that even English syntax suffers from cumbersome inhibitions. I prefer to leave it untranslated.

littled? These are trying experiences for an ex-Indian Army officer. I know . . . I put up with them in France, and I even get a certain bang out of them. But here! Ah! when I think how simple it would be for her to call me "Mahrm'diouk," like everyone else, instead of "Diouki-Diouki!"

Martine senses my feelings and it exasperates her: "If it bothers you, just say so. If you feel uncomfortable with me in the presence of the Duke of Tcheechestaire,[7] I can go home, you know? I suppose you think it is always pleasant for me to listen to what they say in Paris about your mustache or your impossible *prénom!*"

When the altercation reaches this point, I usually, prefer to avoid battle and, beating a prudent retreat, to *filer à la française.*[8] There are moments when one must know how to contain oneself, even at the risk of bursting at the seams. After all, Martine isn't altogether wrong in "looking for" men in this island. Even English women have trouble enough finding them, not only because British education drives them more readily toward the cricket field

‒‒‒‒‒‒‒‒‒‒‒‒‒‒

[7] Normally pronounced "Chich'st'r."
[8] "To take French leave," the normal equivalent of which in French is, as one might expect, *filer à l'anglaise.*

than toward the boudoir,[9] but also because men are considerably less numerous. By some ironical design, which even the most assiduous reading of the Bible can hardly explain, God has seen to it that in this country where women do not especially attract the attention of men, more and more of them should be born every day. French women are all like Martine. When they get to London, they complain that no one looks at them. They simply don't realize that in crossing the Channel they lose 50 per cent of their value.

I must ask to be forgiven: if I speak of women in the language of stockbrokers, it's not altogether without reason. The English woman is like Royal Dutch Shell: she obeys the law of supply and demand. In a country where there's a surplus of three million females, the market quotations are bound to sink. Though we don't have an official

---

[9] Hardly a day goes by without some English woman lodging a complaint with the courts because her husband has been neglecting her for cricket or rugger. Not long ago a Mrs. Joyce Copus sued for divorce on the grounds of "mental cruelty" because her husband had been devoting almost every Saturday and Sunday to cricket and soccer. "No sooner is he back from the office than he bolts his supper and rushes off to play." Mr. Justice Karminsky, however, rejected Mrs. Copus's complaints: "the law not allowing a man to be declared guilty of cruelty for liking cricket too much."

market here, as they do in Timbuktu, you can get a pretty good idea of the bullishness or bearishness of conditions by the reports of recent divorce cases, the market quotations for English women varying with their household value. For the purposes of this evaluation nothing is neglected by our courts—housekeeping, cooking, or laundering. In France a husband who has been abandoned by his wife can get a divorce, but he won't seek to evaluate his financial loss. With us it boils down to a question of *damages*. "Mr. Smith claimed a thousand pounds. Taking into due consideration the value of the wife and the damages incurred by the husband, the judge split the difference and awarded him five hundred pounds." This is how the *News of the World* reports a divorce suit. But it's only natural, isn't it, that in the land of fair play the lover should foot the bill? [10]

Well, it may be normal for us, but it's not for Martine. One day I told her about my good friend Colonel

[10] Quite apart from the "utilitarian" value of his wife, a deceived husband can always claim from the co-respondent—his rival—damages for "loss of connubium." There are times, it must be said, when the magistrates are loth to make a precise value estimate of a wife. "To have to estimate the value of a wife in pounds, shillings, and pence is often delicate and rather nauseous," Judge Gazebrook declared during a divorce trial in which R.A.F. Squadron Leader John Vincent Powell—an ex-Olympic champion—claimed five thousand pounds from Mr. John Mark Fane for depriving him of his wife's company.

Nigel Lesspot (now retired) who had sued his daughter's husband, because she had gotten married without his consent while still a minor. When I explained that he had won his case by proving to the judges that Priscilla's departure had forced him to engage a housekeeper, Martine cried: *"Pays de sauvages!"*

Yet Colonel Lesspot was altogether within his rights. When an Englishwoman abandons her husband, in the eyes of the law it's not just a wife that he's losing; it's first and foremost a housekeeper. That's why on passports or identity cards where "profession" is to be filled in, Martine will write *sans* (none), while an Englishwoman puts *housewife.*

"Décidément," Martine says to me, "it's not the same *planète!"*

Well, perhaps it's a strange planet where, incredible as it may sound to Martine or to Mme Pochet, a wife can sue for divorce on the grounds that her husband has raped her.[11] A strange planet where one day I heard the headmaster of a large public school thus define the ideal spouse

[11] I myself saw a woman obtain a divorce at a London court by explaining that her husband, entering her bedroom by an unlocked door, had abused her at a time when she was unwilling (an exceptional case foreseen in the *Matrimonial Clauses Act*). When the penitent husband spoke of unsatisfied sexual urges, the judge advised him to find some substitute: "Why don't you collect butterflies?" (P.D.)

to his senior boys: "a faithful companion, a nurse, a mother, and a loyal chum." [12]

A chum! In France chumminess kills love. In England a woman is above all a man's chum. When a French girl says to her lover: "Let's remain friends!" it's the end of everything. Here it's the beginning of the rest.

Ah yes, a strange planet where the wife often conserves deep down within her a hidden garden—the garden of *Brief Encounter*—to which her husband never has

---

[12] It was the day of Edward VIII's abdication. The headmaster, who was as grave-faced as he was embarrassed—for the height of embarrassment for an Englishman, when something happens, is to be unable to find a precedent for it—had assembled the boys to hear the King's farewell on the radio. On the desk of the great hall was placed an enormous Bible. Having defined the perfect wife, the headmaster added: "There exists another kind of wife that one should ever be on one's guard against . . . Listen to what St. Paul says about marriage." After reading the misogynic apostle's apologia for celibacy, the headmaster tuned in on the station.

This schoolmaster's definition of the ideal wife may seem peculiar, but it agrees fairly closely with the statistics. Among the chief qualities Englishmen look for in their wives, beauty, elegance, and sex appeal are only mentioned by a very small number (8%) and most of them bachelors, at that. The qualities of "good housewife" (29%) and "good mother" (18%) rate far higher. It is not difficult, therefore—at any rate, for an Englishman—to understand the comment made by a judge who, having to decide a divorce case in which a wife complained of neglect from her husband, declared with a straight face: "The marriage was a happy one, apart from a sexual matter which was always a difficulty."

"What I most look for in a woman is a chum."

access unless one evening in the quiet of the home the reading of the Bible opens its gates!

A strange and inexplicable planet! Perhaps there is even a mystery about this island which I myself cannot explain. Famous biologists have noted it. An inhabitant of an island is different from one of a continent—whether *flora* or *fauna*. If Britannia built her future on the waves, it wasn't, as certain wits have claimed, only because more children are conceived on a Saturday afternoon on the Thames than anywhere else at the same time. Nor was it for love of the Royal Navy. It was because Englishmen, never finding themselves more than sixty miles from the sea, are subjected to the influence of the tides even in the subway. The day that some barbarian conqueror finds a way of lowering the level of the Channel by one hundred and fifty feet in order to attach this island to the Continent, we shall doubtless become for Martine and the Pochets normal people with normal looks. Heaven grant that this day may never dawn and that the Continent may ever preserve, away from it and near it, this unexplainable island-planet!

Dear old England, whose charm and dampness soak into one's skin together! I came back all-repentant and prepared to crave forgiveness from the shades of my ancestors for the affront I caused them in making France my home. I would like to have stayed here longer and to have spent more time pacing the century-old lawns. Above all, I would have wished Martine to develop a certain fondness. But she, like Pochet, is not yet ripe. We must wait and see. . . .

While waiting, I am once again going to abandon dear old England. It's odd how often a subject of Her Most Gracious Majesty can absent himself from England, until the day finally comes when he absents himself for good. For the moment, my fate is linked to that of Daninos and Pochet—and Pochet's got the travel bug. Each spring some press dispatch announcing the imminent plunge of a bathysphere or a new assault on a Himalayan peak produces the same effect on him as the official announcement of the first cuckoo, reported to *The Times* by some retired army colonel in a Shropshire wood, does on millions of sun-starved Britons. Speleologists and frogmen arouse the slumbering explorer in this hearth-loving Frenchman, and he suddenly wishes to participate in the vast expeditions to discover new worlds. While Alpine-climbers and navigators polish up their instruments for assaulting the Great Unknown, Pochet purchases new suitcases and departs for the conquest of lands long, long submerged—by floods of people. He whose father dared extend an adventurous spearhead as far as Pamplona and San Remo now speaks of Stromboli as though it were Montmartre! Oh, how the French animal has changed over the centuries! England, of course, no longer suffices to satisfy this wanderlust; it is at once too near and too remote. Pochet's desire is to go farther and farther afield, and above all farther than Taupin. Fortunately his thirst for travel is quenched easily enough in the bottomless well of his business operations. For Pochet's business activities are the most accom-

modating in the world; they always take him just where
he also wants to go for pleasure. *Il combine les deux choses.*
Thus, having heard that our friend Daninos was planning
a trip to America, he has suddenly discovered a thousand
business reasons for visiting the United States.

And so, there's nothing for it. I'm caught up in the
wheels of this transoceanic operation. I have given Daninos every possible warning on the basis of the experience
of others, but he is still bent on trying to fit the United
States into the Anglo-Saxon world. To keep my end of the
bargain I must go with him and when necessary bail him
out. But, after all, though I feel nothing in common with
the great Yankee democracy, I have nothing against it
either.

And then there's another thing. . . . Daninos and I
have never really seen eye to eye on the subject of our two
countries. But something tells me we may come closer to
doing so by joining forces to criticize a third.

Chapter 10

[P . D .]

THE MAJOR AT SEA

If ever there was a time in his life when the Major was visibly at sea, it must have been during our transatlantic crossing on the S.S. *United States*. No sooner was everyone on board and our things safely stowed away in the cabins, than he set out with Pochet on "an initial reconnaissance of the bar." He was back in half an hour with the announcement that he wanted to go upstairs for a last whiff of fresh British air, so I offered to accompany him.

"It's the damnedest thing, Daninos," he growled, as we emerged on the promenade deck, "but I never thought I'd live to see the day when I would feel like an alien in a British port. Why, right here in Southampton I've discovered the United States. Just look at this great liner that is taking us to New York. It's simply crawling with specimens from all forty-eight states. This motley array of tourists reminds me of wayward lovers. Having paid their dutiful respects to old Aunt Britannia and flirted a bit with the Latin Sisters, they return to their first love. To be sure, they are delighted with the Grand Tour, but they're even happier to be back among their own kind and on their way to regain the only really worthwhile country in the world— the most powerful, the most prosperous, the most beautiful —the United States of America."

It seemed strange to me that the Major should feel such a foreigner among fellow Anglo-Saxons, and I pointed out to him that there were, after all, strong affinities of blood and language binding Britain and America. But he cut me short: "My dear fellow, how on earth do you expect me to feel any affinities for people who call me 'Marm' the first time we meet and ask me how many copies my latest book has sold? As for the language—."

"Now, you cannot deny that you speak the same language?"

"Why yes, Daninos. I do deny it! I deny it completely! Indeed, it's probably this one thing we have in common which most divides us. I was given a shocking example of it a moment ago. Just imagine—at the bar the

steward, a Yankee thoroughbred, if I may be permitted such an outlandish expression, immediately understood Pochet's order, but made me repeat mine!"

I could see by the glint in his eyes and the bristle of his mustache that the Major was really off again, so I made no effort to halt him.

"Yes," he went on, as we paced the deck, "it's really incredible! These people, who hadn't even moved into their present home when we had already been settled for a thousand years on our island, have stolen our language and perverted it. And now they have the nerve to pretend that they don't understand us any more! It's utterly absurd! In fact, I'm told that to hear proper English spoken in the States you have to go to the theater!"

"I don't know," I said, "but I seem to remember a remark by the American theater critic George Jean Nathan: 'After thirty years in the theater I am still wondering if our actors talk and behave like Englishmen, or if Englishmen talk and behave like actors.'"

"Well, what tommyrot! How can you say Americans talk at all? From listening to the passengers on this ship I get the impression that it's not so much words as figures they spout. Ever since I got on board I've heard them do nothing but swap accounts of their trips to Europe. Other tourists often exchange reminiscences that no one can figure out, but American reminiscences have nothing but figures in them! 'In Florence I bought a clip for $10.00! . . . Look at this one—it's exactly the same, only red. I paid $8.50 for it in Rome. . . . And how was your one-month trip? . . . Oh, simply marvelous! . . . We stayed 5½ days in Paris, 3 days in Florence, 4 days in Rome, and 2 in Venice. We usually did a museum in the morning and two monuments in the afternoon. But sometimes Spencer would want to change the schedule, and we'd do a couple of churches in the morning and only one palace in the afternoon. Would you believe it? We covered 10 thousand miles! What a nice trip! [1] In Florence we lived on the *demi-pension* plan. . . . They charged 5,700 lire, but you can get along perfectly well on 5,000. And what about yours?' "

This strange sensation of gobbling figures again struck the Major at our first meal on board, for the consommé was swimming with little numbers from 1 to 9 and all the letters of the alphabet. And he was even more struck by it the next day when the Major and I made the acquaintance of Mr. Cyrus B. Lippcott.

Mr. Lippcott is the kind of American of which there are so many (pardon me, should I say 255,407?). He looks a bit like Harry Truman. He has glistening teeth, pursed lips, a frank glance behind thin metal-rimmed glasses. While Mr. Lippcott, a dealer in grain, did not, like the ex-President, get his start in the world selling suspenders, he did, nevertheless, climb from the bottom to the top rung of the Associated Pork Packers and go on to become head of

----

[1] This word "nice" never fails to crop up in American conversation and is one of the dozen key words in "Basic American." (W.M.T.)

an important section of the Middle West Corn Exchange.[2]
He is clean, he is neat, his shirt is gleaming white, his shoes
are like two sunbeams, his suits are sober—only his ties
have something African about them. But why am I intro-
ducing him, instead of letting him introduce himself, as he
did that first day when he moved his deckchair next to the
Major's and extended a welcoming hand: "Glad to meet
you, Major! My name is Lippcott . . . Cyrus B. Lippcott"?

Reluctant as the Major obviously was to opening up
to a stranger on an American ship, there was nothing he
could do to prevent the other from opening up to him. In
short order, the Major and I learned that Cyrus B. Lippcott would be 51 years old on May 6th; that he was born
in Kansas City, Missouri; that he made $25,000 a year,
owned a 6-room house in Schenectady, New York, and
had a $60,000 life-insurance policy; and that, after marry-
ing first a woman seven years his senior, he had married
a second one who was six years his junior.

"And what about you?" he suddenly fired at the Major.

<hr>

[2] I might add to this description of Daninos's that the American
Who's Who will no doubt describe him in the terms usually reserved for
prominent industrialists: *controls, 1,000 miles gas pipeline, 10 carbon
black plants, also 3 gasoline plants, etc.* (W.M.T.)

The Major was speechless for a moment, and I could tell by the startled look in his eye that he was wondering how on earth the English language—but was it English? —could be used to say so many things in such an incredibly short space of time. In less than four minutes Mr. Lippcott had told us more about himself than a Frenchman does in four months or an Englishman in several generations. In reality, what interested Mr. Lippcott more than anything was to know just how many tigers the Major had shot in his life: 8, 12, or 370?

"H'mm!" grumbled the Major, clearing his throat. "Well now, I don't really know. . . . I've bagged a good-ish number—that I can say for sure—but really, I'm not much interested in the exact figure. It was the fun of the thing, you know, the sport of it that mattered."

"Sure, Major, but what would you figure on the average—two a year?"

"H'mm, h'mm," mumbled the Major, visibly annoyed.

Seeing that he could get no precise information out of him, Mr. Lippcott opened his wallet and pulled out a photograph of a young girl.

"Let me show you a picture of my younger daughter, Major. Her name's Patricia—isn't she a honey?"

"Oh, I say! Jolly fine!" mumbled the Major, awkwardly fingering a photograph showing a young collegiate wearing a sweater with the numeral 6 on it.

"Well," Mr. Lippcott went on, "you'd never believe it, Major. She's only 16 years old and she's already 5 feet 5 inches tall!"

"Five feet six inches, Cyrus!" corrected Mrs. Lippcott, who had just joined us.

"Oh, yes, darling! 5 feet 6 inches! A real nice kid! She's got half a dozen boyfriends and she adores college— it has 2,400 girls and boys . . . and, just think, it's only 166 miles from where we live, so we can see her twice a month. A real nice place!"

It was apparent from the Major's flustered expression that this first exposure to Mr. Lippcott and his family was enough for the time being, and he got to his feet muttering something about "taking a stroll" and "getting his sea-legs."

"Good lord, Daninos," he said when we were safely out of earshot, "I need a good lungful of numerically unpolluted fresh air before I go down to my cabin."

But unfortunately for the Major, there was no escape. The numbers pursued him relentlessly, for when we stepped into the hall of the promenade deck we came face to face with a handsome blackboard listing in bold white letters the main events of the day. The day's film was announced:

LADY CYNTHIA'S PASSION [*112 Minutes*]
[*Trucolor*]

"Well, if that doesn't take the cake!" muttered the Major. "I can well understand an American who has to know that Lady Cynthia's passion is going to last one hundred and twelve minutes before going in to see a film on board ship. His time is limited, and he might have a train to catch. But my own indifference—on the Atlantic, or anywhere else—as to whether Lady Cynthia's passion lasts a quarter of an hour or an hour and fifty-two minutes can mean only one thing, Daninos. I'm just not made to be an American!"

Chapter 11

[P . D .]

THE NUMBERS-MEN

The impression of living among numbers-men was one that both the Major and I experienced not only on the boat, but frequently thereafter in the United States.

Cyrus B. Lippcott, with whom we had struck up a friendship despite the basic divergence of outlook between him and Marmaduke, had arranged to meet us in the bar at the Park Lane Hotel in New York. The first thing that struck us in the monumental bar was a sign warning us:

THE PRESENCE
OF MORE THAN 388 PERSONS
IS DANGEROUS AND UNLAWFUL[1]

The Major made a rapid panoramic survey of the room, no doubt to evaluate the number of persons present —it was not 388—and then ordered a whisky. He was brought a bottle of Grant's Aged Scotch that bore a white label marked "4,207,680 minutes." Why 4,207,680 minutes? Because the chief merit of this whisky is that it is 8 years old, and for an American 4,207,680 minutes make 8 years as easily as 4 times 8 make 32.

Mr. Lippcott, however, expressed a preference for champagne.

"Bring me a Chandon-Moët '52," he said, after pulling out of his wallet a curious little card covered with figures where Bordeaux, Burgundies, ports, and champagnes were rated from 0 (No Good) to 7 (The Best) for the years 1931 to 1955.

"You see," he said to me, " '52 rates a 6, so it's okay."

~~~~~~~~~~~~~~~~~~~~

[1] I say 388, and not 350 or 400, and I invite the skeptics to visit the Park Lane and verify the figure themselves. It may mean a bit of a trip, but it's worth it.

1 5 7

All this was a source of wonder to the Major, to me, and, most of all, to my wife, Sonia. Sonia is the sort of person who when giving me a telephone number says: "It's Trocadero eight, two, something," or when speaking of the population of the United States says: "A good 120-50 million, no?" She just isn't made of the same stuff as Mr. Cyrus B. Lippcott who never speaks of a Picasso, but of a $30,000 Picasso, who doesn't talk of a building, but of a $2,000,000 building, a 75,000-volume library, or a 38-room chateau. Even of a man he will often say: "He's a $150- or a $500-a-week man." All this the Major accepts with a smile, though it goes against his grain. But what he positively can't stomach is to hear Lippcott say of his poodle: "It's a $700 dog, you know."

Never, Marmaduke insists, would a well-bred Englishman dream of mentioning the price in the presence of his dog.

A European is sometimes shocked when an American who has been introduced to him barely a minute before asks him how much he earns a year or how much he paid for his suit. The Major regards this as shockingly ill-bred. But he's mistaken. It's simply the result of a very different breeding. If you don't openly disclose how much money you are making, it means that you are trying to hide something from your neighbor, that you are displaying a dismal lack of that spirit of mutual trust and co-operation which goes into the making of a "100 per cent American." It is something that is instilled in you at school along with the notion of numbers.

At the tender age when the French child learns that his ancestors the Gauls lived in huts built on piles and wore long, handle-bar mustaches, the American child learns that there were 102 Pilgrims on board the *Mayflower* when she sailed from Plymouth on the 6th of September 1620, and that these 102 pioneers, after completing a voyage of 3,200 miles in 66 days, were to grow into a nation of 166 million, with an annual budget of $66.3 billion.

The American child may be late in learning to read, but he is early in learning to count. He has the billion in his blood long before the alphabet.[2] At an age of forty and some odd years, I still have only the vaguest notion of what a billion is. I must go to the dictionary to find out whether

~~~~~~~~~~~~~

[2] One of the largest and oldest banks in the United States, the Bank of America of San Francisco ($9,000,000,000 in deposits), distributes small savings banks to students in the high schools enabling them to open bank accounts as early as they want. The contents of these small boxes are collected each month by the bank. Most American children, rich or poor, earn their pocket money in their extracurricular hours by delivering newspapers or working as gardener's assistants, grocery boys, caddies, restaurant waiters, or bellhops, etc.

it is 2 million or 100 million. Every American child knows what it is, just as we French used to know that a *sou* (5 centimes) was a *sou*.

Personally, figures have always wearied me. When *The New York Times*, for example, informs me that the revenue of the city of New York, for the first quarter of the fiscal year beginning July 1st, was $469,097,383, as compared to the $462,941,874 of the preceding year, I find myself swimming in a vast porridge of figures. If I were told it was $888,983,566 or $602,500,343, it would be all the same to me. I feel no urge to subtract one from the other to find the difference; rather, I feel like subtracting myself from the subtraction to see if there isn't something else in the newspaper to read about. But it's no use; an American paper is the last thing to read if you want to escape figures. There are more figures in a single copy of *The New York Times* than in 700 copies of any French daily.

I have kept a copy of the paper I bought the evening of our meeting with Lippcott at the Park Lane, when I came back to the hotel with my head still reeling with figures. Everywhere I looked I met numbers:

2 MILES OF PIERS SET FOR BROOKLYN
IN 7 YEAR PROJECT
$85,000,000 CONTRACT

FORD MOTOR COMPANY:
$2,000,000,000
INDUSTRIAL EMPIRE

PRESIDENT BETTER:
46 MINUTE TALK
WITH 5 AIDES

Nothing escaped the all-powerful figure—neither the Protestant churches that had distributed $1,000,000,000 through 3,000 welfare agencies to succor 11,000,000 needy; nor the 5,200,383 inhabitants of the state of New Jersey, who had taken orderly refuge in 63,483 air-raid shelters under the supervision of 250,000 wardens in a civil defense exercise announced at 6:00 P.M. by 809 sirens; nor the Ford Empire, now worth $2,000,000,000 after starting out 53 years ago on an initial cash investment of $28,000; nor the 57,475 fans who saw the Lions of Detroit trounce the Bears of Chicago when the 6-foot 9-inch, 21-year-old end, Jim Maloney, plunged over the goal line on a 12-yard pass in the game's fourth period for a winning score of 26 to 19; nor even the stomach of the late William Woodward, Jr., who was accidentally shot by his wife (the body of the 35-year-old multimillionaire sportsman being found to contain only 0.065 per cent alcohol, whereas the intoxication level is legally fixed at 0.15 per cent).

In the land of Cyrus B. Lippcott there is not a word, not a gesture, not an act that cannot be reduced to numbers. Everthing is measurable: the work of a writer ("Damon Runyon made half a million dollars with 75,000 words"); the efficiency of the Roman Catholic Church, with its coefficient of 82.5 per cent almost equaling that of Standard Oil; the maximum length of a kiss on the movie screen (40 inches of film); or the number of calories needed to read *Gone with the Wind.*

The people of the United States believe in numbers as the Arabs in the Koran. Thanks to numbers, Americans recently discovered that the consumption of water in the United States between 9.00 and 9.30 P.M. which had remained constant for 35 years had noticeably increased in the last two. Why? Because of television. And why because of television? Because 60 million Americans, being forced by the new divinity to remain seated from 7.00 to 9.00 P.M., simultaneously use their bathrooms now from 9.00 to 9.30 P.M.

Oh Homo Americanus, you are a number lost in a sea of numbers, humble or colossal, you live and die a number—from the $2000-a-week executive to the $86-a-week counter-man! The composer George Gershwin once organized a dinner in Hollywood where the guests were announced by their weekly earnings. At a banquet given

Cyrus B. Lippcott reading The New York Times.

in honor of Pandit Nehru in New York to which the cream of American industry was invited, a businessman said to him: "Do you realize, Mr. Prime Minister, how much is represented at this table? I just added it up. You are eating dinner with at least 20 billion dollars."

From the heights of the pyramids, forty centuries looked down on Napoleon's armies. From the lowliness of their chairs, twenty billions looked up at Nehru.

Even what I was at that very moment doing was, I discovered, numerable and numbered. For the *Christian Science Monitor* informed me that the average American absorbs twelve and a half inches of international news and a good yard and a half of sport news a day.

Having learned that the human eye devours the type at the rate of two tenths of an inch a second, I was busy calculating—in true American style—that our friend Lippcott must consume some 30 yards and 33 inches of comics every Sunday, when Major Thompson burst unexpectedly into my room: "What did I tell you, Daninos, about these people having such deplorable manners! Look at this!"

He handed me a copy of the evening paper, whose glaring headlines proclaimed:

MEG SAW G.C. 3 TIMES
157 MINUTES YESTERDAY

Actually, the Major was not particularly excited by the fact that Princess Margaret had seen Group Captain Townsend three times the day before and that they had talked for a total of 157 minutes. But what made him positively explode was that these Yankees should push familiarity to the point of calling the Queen's sister: "Meg."

Chapter 12

[P . D .]

WHAT IS AN AMERICAN?

I must make a confession: when I told myself, on arriving in the United States, that there were 166 million Americans, that they could fit France 17 times over into their country, and that I must write something about them, I felt like going straight back to my bed in Paris. I was seized by dizziness. My eyes blurred. I felt faint.

But Major Thompson came to the rescue: "Calm yourself, old boy! You're raising a storm in a teacup. The biggest teacup in the world, I'll grant you, but what of it? You'll see, the United States is the most transparent nation on the globe. The first couple of days here I, too, felt quite bowled over by the immensity of it all. The most frightening thing, of course, was the figure—166,000,000 inhabitants! But you must never let yourself be overawed by figures. You may remember that when I had to size up 43 million Frenchmen I resorted to division. Here it's even simpler: a subtraction will do.

"Now there's nothing like a citizen of the Middle West to show you how to do this subtraction properly, and since you're lucky enough to find in our friend Cyrus B. Lippcott a native of Kansas City, Missouri, go ask him to enlighten you."

The Major, as usual, was right. To Cyrus B. Lippcott the center of gravity of the U.S.A. and the solar system is Kansas City. And the heart of America, its very flesh and soul, is the Midwest. The rest is peanuts.

It took Cyrus a bare half-hour to clear up the situation. To deal with 166 million Americans he resorted to the method of the Indian head-shrinkers. He took out a bag of Michigan flat beans and spilled them out in front of me on a large table, giving them the approximate shape of the United States. Then, having crunched up Alaska and a few of the Aleutians—to be excluded from any meaningful representation of the U.S.A.—he began his demonstration:

TAKE A TOTAL POPULATION OF . . . *166 million Americans*

A Now New York isn't the United States; so we must start by excluding from the total the population of Manhattan and its suburbs, making . . . .   *15 million*

B In view of the strangeness and abnormal behavior of the people of Texas, who give their Lone Star flag precedence over the Stars and Stripes, they, too, have no place in any generalization about the United States; so let's be on the safe side and count out these . . . .   *8 million*

C The Bostonians, who can tell you the quickest way of getting from Piccadilly to Buckingham Palace, but don't know where Kansas City is, along with most of the inhabitants of New England, who are more English than American, obviously can't provide a basis for any real picture of America; so we eliminate another . . . .   *9 million*

D The Negroes, the Germans, the Italians, the Chinese, the Japanese, and the Jews can't be considered pureblood Americans either; so we must knock out another . . . .   *22 million*

E It would also be misleading to in-
clude in the total those Americans
who, though American citizens, were
born abroad; that is . . . .   *10 million*

F Certain borderland states, like Ari-
zona, New Mexico, Oregon, Montana,
and North Dakota, though they're
states of the Union, can only give
foreigners a false picture of the coun-
try; so better omit their . . . .   *9 million*

G For different, though equally valid,
reasons the much too cosmopolitan
populations of cities such as Washington, Hollywood, and Chicago, in
addition to the Spanish, French and
Asiatic elements found in cities such
as San Francisco and New Orleans,
can only mess up a clear idea of the
real United States; so we exclude an-
other . . . .   *7 million*

H Just for the record, let's make a passing reference to the Indians, carefully holed up in their reservations.
We can take out this residue of . . . .   *350 thousand*

Which means we must subtract from the
total . . . .   *166 million*
approximately . . . .   *— 80 million*

LEAVING ....   86 *million*
    among whom we must eliminate all
    minors, the senile, and impotent citi-
    zens, or some ....   — *44 million*
Which is to say that there remain, by
and large (or rather by and small) .... *42 million Americans*

Forty-two million—no more than the population of France (minus Montmartre and Montparnasse)! You see, the U.S.A. isn't really such a frightening problem, after all!"

Still, even if we limit the number of real, *genuine* Americans to 42 million, how are we to define the *Homo Americanus?*

Even the Major was a little reticent when I put the question to him. I had doubtless attributed to him affinities with his distant transatlantic cousins which he just didn't have. He was certainly right about the language: it divides the Anglo-Saxons rather than unites them. And what the Americans have done to the language of Shakespeare, they have done to their people. Americans do not render what they borrow; they render it American. The great mystery and miracle of this country, more than any other, is how it brands each individual with the same indelible mark, whether he comes from Frankfurt, Buda-

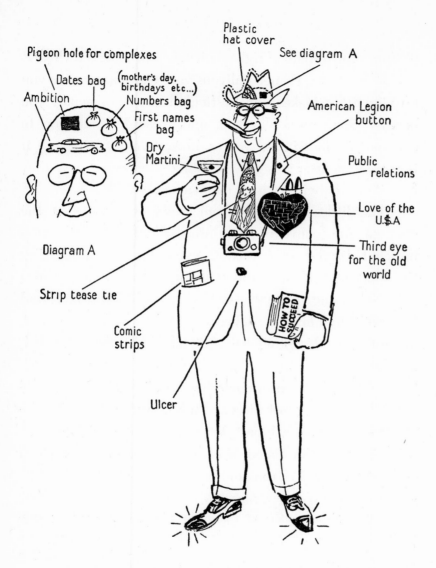

Pigeon hole for complexes

Dates bag

(mother's day, birthdays etc...)

Ambition

Numbers bag

First names bag

Dry Martini

Diagram A

Strip tease tie

Comic strips

Ulcer

Plastic hat cover

See diagram A

American Legion button

Public relations

Love of the U.$.A

Third eye for the old world

X-ray photograph of C.B.L., American Citizen

pest, or Amsterdam. England makes you reserved, Switzerland dulls you, France enlivens you, Germany makes you heavier, Italy makes you gesticulate, Sweden makes you healthy, Spain ennobles you, and Ireland drives you to drink—but the United States makes you American.[1] It is as though, after a mighty shuffling of chromosomes, they manufacture their products on an assembly line.

The little immigrant from Budapest arrives at the start of the conveyor belt stoop-shouldered, scrawny-muscled, black-haired, anxious-eyed. He then undergoes the treatment of milk and wide-open spaces, free enterprise and orange juice, the dollar and the carrot, facts and figures. Vitaminized, deluxized, Sanforized, orlonized, Simonized, chlorophyllized, fluidized, classified, labeled, and asepticized, the new arrival is at last metamorphized. The American way of life overhauls him. At the end of the assembly line, a generation and a half later, out comes the finished product—a blond, long-boned, lean-necked, narrow-hipped, milky faced, short-haired Johnny or Barbara ready to chant: "I'm 100 per cent American!"

wwwwwwwwwwwwwww

[1] With the exception, of course, of British subjects. As Alistair Cooke has noted, one speaks of Irish-Americans, German-Americans, Polish-Americans, Swedish-Americans, Italo-Americans, Greco-Americans, but never of Anglo-Americans. (W.M.T.)

A mystery, all right, though a mystery that can doubtless be explained in terms of environment, the effect of the climate, cross-breeding, high schools, food, and, even more, by the strange phenomenon of mimicry coupled with the immigrant son's haunting fear of not becoming American, talking American, thinking American.

Still it's a mystery.

How can I doubt for a moment that our friend Cyrus B. Lippcott is not the product of this mystery? But that doesn't help to define him.

Oh, Cyrus, you who bear in your veins the blood of the MacCulloughs and the Finkelsteins, a pint of Alpestrini and of Montezuma, a bowlful of Ehrenkreuz and a drop of Dupleix, how can I possibly define you?

How can I define a citizen who had a grandmother that was Irish, another that was German, an American father, and a Dutch mother? Unless it is by comparing the cross-section of his brain to that of the French Chamber of Deputies—Ireland occupying roughly the place of the Social Republicans, England that of the Communists, Germany that of the M.R.P., and the Jews that of the Poujadistes?

I sometimes explain the stern side of your character by recalling that one of your ancestors was a certain Patience Peacock[2] who came over—and how proud you are of it!—on the *Mayflower* (no doubt about it, if the *Mayflower* had really carried all those whom present-day Americans claim as their forebears, she would have had to be as big as the *Queen Elizabeth*).

From Finkelstein, who began his career selling suspenders on street corners and ended it on the top floor of a skyscraper as the Underwear King, you doubtless get that astonishing aptitude for making good in grain after going bust in pork. To Signora Bianchetta Alpestrini, your grandfather's wife and the daughter of a Catania greengrocer, you must owe your predilection for *pasticciata* and the Sicilian restaurants of Greenwich Village. But how can I fail to admire the way in which so many heterogeneous origins have managed to bring forth products as specifically American as you and your blonde child, the aerodynamic Patricia, whose voice, bearing, and looks have something in common with all the millions of other American high-school girls?

What do you have in common with those first colonists who made your country?

Those frontier wood-choppers, those pioneers, those

~~~~~~~~~~~~~~~~~~~

[2] The Puritans were wont to give their daughters "virtues" for Christian names: Patience, Chastity, Fidelity, Silence.

"I wouldn't dream of giving my daughter to a man who hasn't been American for at least three centuries!"

blizzard-hardened trappers who scorned the English love of comfort have become cold-shunning citizens more comfort-craving than any Thompson. Those austere Puritans, who once condemned all unnecessary prattle about cooking, now give anything to belong to *Gourmet-Connoisseur*'s clubs and to see their film stars' favorite dishes on TV.[3] Those would-be settlers, many of whom traveled six thousand miles to find new lands into which to sink new roots, now move ceaselessly from one home to the next (32 million Americans change their addresses every year).

Those individualists who abandoned their families, their homelands, their customs, to go and live alone and far from everything, now have a passion for doing everything in groups: "Join us for a drink. . . . Join us for a party. . . . Join us for a vacation." Solitude is a plague. The solitary individual is suspect. The American is judged a singular being if he doesn't know how to live in the plural. Let him drink, go out, sing, travel, amuse himself, and even shave—but never alone! Pochet discovered this one morning on the Chicago-Los Angeles train when Cyrus B. Lippcott hailed him and a fellow passenger: "Join us for a shave, Al!" Whereupon he dragged the be-

~~~~~~~~~~~~~~~~~~~~

[3] "What could be more appetizing," Mr. Fred MacMurray himself declared on the radio, "than two fried eggs proudly casting their limpid gold eyes upon you?"

wildered Pochet into a washroom where half a dozen others seemed delighted to be brushing their teeth, taking showers, and shaving together.

Have the Americans perhaps become the opposite of what they were?

Those democrats who made equality the cornerstone of their constitution are today addicted to discrimination. It is relatively harder for a young girl to be admitted to the Bachelors' Cotillion in Baltimore than to be received at Buckingham Palace. Mme Pochet, who thought she would have no more trouble obtaining an invitation to the Assembly Ball in Philadelphia than she does to the annual ball at the Elysée Palace in Paris, had to repack her lamé evening gown because she could not claim even indirect descent from one of George Washington's officers. By Lafayette, she swore, never would she set foot again in this *maudit* city where a Colonial Dame, armed with a formidable *Social Register,* had treated her to an exercise in subtraction even more impressive than Cyrus B. Lippcott's—by reducing the number of bona fide Americans to 2,733. For many people in the world it's the height of distinction to know as many people as possible. But for certain Philadelphia and Boston ladies the be-all and the end-all of life is to know nobody, or, at least, to recognize nobody as being anybody. When the same Philadelphia

Colonial Dame who humiliated Mme Pochet was handed a list of those invited by the Kelly family to a reception honoring Grace before the wedding, she gave it a sharp scrutiny and then exclaimed, delighted: "I know none of these people!"

In American conversation the words "exclusive," "most exclusive," and "restricted" recur so ceaselessly that Pochet sometimes wonders if the secret dream of Cyrus B. Lippcott isn't the creation of an ultra-exclusive club, a club so private that all Americans would be excluded from it but himself. Those stout lovers of independence who fled the strict etiquette and the humiliations of the European Courts suffer today from the frustrations of a Principality complex, and they would gladly exchange their blast furnaces for a *de* or a *von* as they chase desperately after the thing they want most—an aristocracy.[4]

_____

[4] Lacking authentic quarterings of nobility, Americans resort to such substitutes as: the numbering of the descendants of famous dynasties (Henry Ford II, J. D. Rockefeller III), the attribution of privileged seats in the most-chic restaurants and nightclubs (at El Morocco the "Siberia" in the Champagne Room is "high class"; at Sardi's the bench is *the* place to sit—usually the gentleman seated nearest to the powder room is a nobody); the numbering of license plates (the lower they are the better —AC 1 is excellent); the classification of cars themselves (some people even rank a Chrysler before a Cadillac: its resale value is less, thus it offers a better indication of the financial unconcern of the owner—only rich and famous people can afford to run around in very old and small

cars.) Finally, the *Social Register* takes the place of an *Almanach de Gotha* or a *Burke's Peerage*. Certain states have their own aristocratic classification according to a fixed order of social or financial seniority; in Texas, cotton precedes livestock, and both of them come before oil (*nouveau riche*). In most great cities the annual debutante balls are scenes of merciless battles which are fought between the *nouveaux riches* and the stately dames of the Board of Governors which controls the admissions.

Chapter 13

[P.D.]

THE LOCOMOTIVE-MEN

The day after my arrival in New York, I woke up to find a man in red looking at me jeeringly. It was the first time such a thing had ever happened to me, and it was unnerving. It's quite something to come to New York expecting to wake up to a view of Rockefeller Center and to find planted in front of you, instead, a man in red wearing a baseball cap and motorist's gloves!

I sat up with a jerk and, opening my eyes wider, I realized that the man was not exactly at the foot of my bed, but a few yards away; he was looking at me through the window from the top of a skyscraper that was going up next door. I quickly realized that there would be no hope of peace and quiet in this room, so I decided to ask the management for another.

On the north side the situation was much calmer—the first day, at any rate. But at the crack of dawn on the second I was awakened by a mighty roar of trucks and cranes. They were starting to tear down the obsolete building opposite. It's the law of existence in New York: everything is either going up or coming down—houses, jobs, gadgets, celebrities, topics of conversation.

I still cannot decide which is the more ghastly of the two noises, but I think the roar of demolition is even worse than the racket of construction. The former begins with the hammering of pneumatic drills digging into the ground and piercing the walls. Then immense cranes carry off whole floors. In the space of a few seconds I saw a living-room, a dining-room, and two bathrooms borne away. It is all so well done that you are surprised not to see anyone being carried off at the same time. You even wonder how the building ever held together.

Preferring to hear and see people build rather than destroy, I went back to the wing I had previously occupied. This time I got a room on the twenty-fourth floor, and I figured I had a six-day head start on the enemy (who was rising at the rate of one story every two days). A friendly enemy, to be sure, for over the intervening abyss

I had established contact with the little man in red: he is called Benedict Camacho, is 37 years old, has 2 children, a 1955 Chevrolet, and a $10,000 life-insurance policy, and makes $110 a week.

Contrary to my stupid calculations, which had failed to take into account the all-American passion for breaking records, Benedict Camacho was yesterday once more on the same level as my table. At three in the afternoon he had overtaken me. Tomorrow I shall see only his feet. I would gladly go up another floor, but mine is the top one. Above me there is only the "roof," reserved for parties, receptions, and evening dancing. Which means that when the workers knock off at five in the afternoon (I don't know how those people get down from such heights, but they vanish in the twinkling of an eye), I have a bare half-hour of respite. At five-thirty the *party* begins—with jazz, and then with the cha-cha-cha—which I find less than cha-cha-charming.

At any rate, according to my calculations (good or bad) in eight days it will all be over.

Major Thompson, however, proved less patient than I. He claims that it's always risky associating with people before they've properly settled in. Besides, he says he can't sleep comfortably unless he is sure of waking up in the same place the next morning. Marmaduke, therefore, left the hotel and the city, declaring to the desk as he went: "I shall return, gentlemen, when you are built."

And he moved on to the only city in the United States which is more or less bearable for a subject of Her Majesty—Boston. This impregnable citadel of American Anglomania has managed to beat the British at the game of numbering houses. Imagine the Major's surprise when he discovered between No. 8 and No. 14 on Beacon Street a dwelling numbered 10½. And as though this weren't enough, he then espied through its large paned windows solemn, whiskered gentlemen snoozing in deep black-leather armchairs under copies of *The Times*—exactly as though they were in the Cavalry Club on Piccadilly.[1]

One can get used to anything in life—even to the hurly-burly of New York. None of this would have mattered much if it hadn't been for the electricity. Paris is regarded, often mistakenly, as the *ville lumière,* but New York is really and truly the *ville electricité*. It is, at any rate, the first I have ever really made sparks in. In New

[1] The place in question was the Boston Athenaeum, a private library whose 1,049 members find ample time to indulge in the favorite pastime of Bostonians—genealogy—and to discuss the dates of their respective arrivals in the city. When you ask a Bostonian how long he has been living in Boston, he replies quite simply: "since 1702," as though he and his ancestors were one.

York there is electricity everywhere—in the doorhandles of taxis, in hotel doorknobs, between two sheets of paper, in your hair, in the Major's mustache, in everything.[2]

When Sonia, who arrived several days after me, came up to my room, she found me dressed in my underpants and wearing gloves, to say nothing of a little chain around my neck which linked me to the floor. She immediately realized that something was up. I explained to her that the air of New York was so dry and so saturated with electricity that the only thing to do was to be properly grounded at all times.

"You are joking?" she said.

To prove to her that I wasn't, I took off my gloves and embraced her. She immediately felt the shock and bade me keep my distance.

I then amused myself—if I can so call it—by making a few sparks, just to convince her. I opened a closet here and closed a door there. I have done many things in my life. Making electricity is, after all, an occupation like any other, if only it weren't so painful. I was continuing my

wwwwwwwwwwww

[2] The air of New York is so dry that room humidifiers are in great demand. Everything is so charged with electricity that the toll bridges have antennas sticking up from the road to make contact with the chassis of each car, thus sparing the toll collector the pain of an electric shock as he picks up the fare.

demonstration when the telephone rang. As I had forgotten to put my gloves back on I received the communication in the fingers.[3]

"You get on my nerves!" said Sonia. And she left to go shopping. New York, she told me, had some *formidable* things in orlon. She had already seen some petticoats: "and, you know, half the price of what they are in Paris." It is really extraordinary how expensive Paris can sud-

wwwwwwwwwwwww

[3] I can well imagine the reader's disbelief over this episode, and particularly over this chain business. In his place I, too, would feel that the author had gone a bit far. Shall I confess that I hesitated a long time before including it? "That chain," I said to myself, "will take a lot of swallowing." In fact, many people smiled when I told them the story. Well, in reality, the chain that I might have invented had already been forged in real life—so true is it that if there is real life in fiction, there is even more fiction in real life. To convince the skeptics let me give them a résumé of a lecture given not long ago at the Western Reserve University Hospital by Professor George J. Thomas of Pittsburgh, the text of which was obligingly passed on to me (when I was already back in Europe) by Professor Jean-Marie Verne, a Paris hospital surgeon: static electricity in the United States brings death to more than 100 persons a year—killed in operating-rooms by the explosion of anesthetic gases. The simple rubbing of a nylon slip or the moving of an anesthetic apparatus can cause a catastrophe. Many precautions are thus taken to limit— though they cannot entirely eliminate—the number of accidents. Each piece of furniture, from the operating-table to wheelchairs, must be connected to the floor *by a small chain,* and everything that is insulated from the ground must be linked to it by some metallic connection or by a wet cloth (including the person to be operated on, who can, if he rests on an insulating rubber mattress, become charged with static electricity).

denly become when a French woman wants to buy something abroad!

Apart from the electricity you find in your hotel room —which varies with the amount of steel used in the framework[4]—I always have the impression in New York of being plugged into a high-tension current. The sensation is aggravated if, as was my case, you have just come from Geneva. All of which makes me wonder if the best way to appreciate the United States is not to begin the trip in Switzerland.

Let me explain. When I arrive in Geneva, I feel an invisible hand slowing down my motor. I could almost swear that the stationmaster of Cornavin had given me a dose of quinine. In New York the dose becomes an injection of electricity. Something here speeds you up. No matter where you go, you go quickly. There is a certain New York rhythm you fall in with immediately, whether you are going to buy pajamas at Saks or to blow up the safe-deposit vaults of the First National City Bank.

Strolling is something that has no meaning in New York. In Paris you stroll down the rue du Chat-qui-Pêche

wwwwwwwwwwwwww

[4] It also depends on your footwear, the leather moccasin leading the field.

wondering whether you are going to end up in the rue de la Huchette or come out on the quai Saint-Michel. But you don't stroll in a city where you are certain of finding 57th Street between 56th and 58th. Who is tempted to write a poem on graph paper?

Americans in general and New Yorkers in particular are veritable human locomotives that go non-stop from seven in the morning till midnight. (The American wife is a super-locomotive that drags her husband after her at a great pace, and the men must be sure to be well hitched if they want to avoid accidents.)

One of the most revealing books, in my opinion, on the American mentality is a children's book called *Tootle the Engine,* by Gertrude Crampton. *Tootle the Engine* tells you more about the U.S.A. than Tocqueville, Fenimore Cooper, Faulkner, and Hemingway combined.

Tootle is a young locomotive which, like every loco-motive-kid in Engineville, goes to the locomotive school and learns the ABC of every well-brought-up locomotive: stop at the red flag and keep to the rails. Only in this way can she become a great lady, I mean, a great streamliner. Like many of her classmates, Tootle begins her notebooks well. Her columns are straight and she sticks to the ap-pointed lines. And then one day, at the end of a term, just as spring is beginning to burst out all over, Tootle discovers the joy of straying from the rails and running off to pick daisies.

The locomotive-superior, I mean, the principal of the the Engineville school, is very worried. After consigning Tootle to the depot, she decides to call a town meeting, throws a "danger" signal, and swings into action. Tootle is allowed to come out again. Once again she is seized by a longing to pick daisies, and she leaves the rails. But the moment she goes to pick a daisy, she meets a flag. She goes over to the other side of the track, bends over, and again a red flag looms up before her. Everywhere the hostile landscape bristles with red flags. All the flowers have become stop signals, for all the locomotive-citizens have co-operated and banded together to make Tootle return to the straight path—which she does on seeing before her the green signal of the open track. She will become a great streamliner.

Tootle is all America, with its conventions, conformism, "danger" signals, wailing of sirens, town meetings, co-operation, and, above all, train spirit—the train one must take, the train of existence, the American way of life. The American lives on rails, and if he is ever tempted to run off and pick daisies, he is immediately called to order by invisible red flags that are more imperative than any rocket signal.[5]

He can, of course, express doubts about the spirit of the Constitution, declare that he doesn't believe in God, wear suede shoes,[6] sport a colored shirt for dinner, and choose to live in a "bad" quarter of town (one that is inhabited by, or is close to, Puerto Ricans, Chinamen, and Negroes). But he will be classed as a suspicious character, an individual to be avoided, one who is perversely bent on pursuing the wrong road. As for his habitation, it will be said, in the best railway style, that he lives "on the wrong side of the tracks."[7]

A few hours in New York and you, too, will be in-

ˎˎˎˎˎˎˎˎˎˎˎˎˎˎˎˎˎˎ

[5] It should be noted that the longing to pick daisies is quickly curbed by poison ivy, a venomous plant growing all over the United States which provokes a violent itch and an irritating skin rash.

[6] Major Thompson, who sometimes wears suede shoes, was one day asked by a most polite young man if he was A.C.-D.C. These letters do not, as the Major thought at first, designate a decoration, but are abbreviations for "Alternating Current-Direct Current." They refer to those homosexuals who are not afraid of women. The Major, who cares little for what others may think of him, went on wearing suede shoes in the U.S.A. whenever he felt like it.

[7] This often-heard American expression originates from the fact that many towns in the U.S.A. are divided by a railway track separating the "residential" quarter from the poor quarter.

corporated in the railroad schedule and become a part of
the network. Consciously or unconsciously you become
yourself a little train, mindful of the timetables and the
switches.

Take for example those "express-waiters" in the
restaurants and drugstores.[8] The easy-going European
method generally employed by Sonia or Mme Pochet: "I
think I'll take a grapefruit and then a steak and then . . .
on thinking it over, better give me some smoked salmon oh!
. . . and well, no! . . . a grapefruit" cannot be adopted
here without risking a catastrophe. The moment you begin
enumerating "a grapefruit, a steak," the "express-waiter"
charts your itinerary on his little green pad (in duplicate).
If you change your mind halfway through, you will see his
face darken and frown.

It's the same story with those numerous specialists
you have to deal with in the hotels. You just can't stop the
first flunky going by and give him your dirty laundry, your
shoes, a pair of trousers to be pressed, and a button to be
sewn on. I have seldom seen a face as put out as the Irish
chambermaid's when Pochet handed her a pair of shoes
his first day in New York. You could have sworn she had

──────────

[8] I am not talking, of course, of those New York restaurants that
are more French than American, where you have time to kill reflecting
on what you are going to eat. I am talking of feeding-places.

never touched that kind of merchandise in her life. The valet, a distinguished looking gentleman, considered the shoes in his turn without touching them, and then said to Pochet in a rather scornful tone: "Call the barbershop."

For a moment Pochet was left wondering if in the United States shoes are given shampoos. Calling up the barber about a pair of shoes may seem strange to a foreigner. But it seemed stranger still to the valet that this ignorant foreigner, from God knows where, should not know that the express shoeshine boy is stationed at the barber's.

Chapter 14

THE REALM
OF WRAPPING PAPER

You might think that the "land of the locomotive-men," as Daninos has just called it, was the fastest in the world, and many people have this idea of the United States. But I must state that it is at once true and false. It is sometimes the fastest, but often the slowest, too—as in the case of the trains themselves. As for American cars, they are made to go 120 miles an hour, but can rarely do more than 60 because of speed limits. Pochet, who was delighted to get behind the steering wheel of his new de luxe machine in New York, had to travel the distance between Paris and Timbuktu before he could find a state where he could hit

110. By the time he had reached Nevada, he had lost his appetite for speed.

Yes, really! The United States is a strange country where everything is made to go faster than anywhere else and where everything seems organized to go more slowly (the only thing that goes damnably fast is the dollar, which disappears from one's pocket at an almost supersonic velocity).

The almost incessant use of pencil and paper contributes to the slowdown. Americans, who have a reputation for being machines, spend a considerable part of their existence writing, even while driving. Various and sundry acts that elsewhere require nothing in writing, here have to be carefully committed to paper.

When I take a taxi in Paris, the driver may make me get out because I am not going in his direction. But if he agrees to take me, the first thing he does is drive me to the desired address without further ado. But in New York the first thing a taxi-driver does is take out a pencil and pad and note down the time, the place he picked me up, and the address I've given him. Sometimes, to be sure, he writes this all down while driving, which adds a dash of excitement to it all. Bus-drivers, too, go in for a strange kind of bookkeeping which the simple-minded foreigner has difficulty fathoming.

Even in dining-cars you are required to write out your order on a pad (with carbon copy). As the handwriting of Europeans is often illegible, Mme Pochet was obliged, while traveling on the City of Denver (Union Pacific Railways) to ask for her steak by printing her order, which made her furious. It unleashed a tirade against American cooking.

"That they do not know how to season a salad is pardonable," she declared. "But that they dare to call 'French Dressing' this mixture of cream, tomato, and *vinaigre—ça non!*"

Pochet immediately chimed in to say that people who, thanks to their freezers, sometimes make a steak wait three months to be eaten and drink *café au lait* with their oysters cannot be taken seriously. At which point a Negro waiter proudly opened a bottle of California wine, labeled: "Special Red Sparkling Burgundy, Beware of Imitations." This was more than Pochet could stomach. He couldn't swallow another bite.

Here, in every field, paper is king. American waiting-rooms, like American offices, are strewn with memoranda, notepads, pencils. As soon as he has a spare moment in his office, between two memos dictated to his secretary, our friend Cyrus B. Lippcott loves to doodle away at little geometric designs while talking or telephoning. Moreover, he keeps them because, he explained to me, in case of a nervous breakdown or a simple check-up,[1] these squares and circles, being a pure emanation of the subconscious, will provide his psychoanalyst with precious clues.

Like all Americans, Lippcott is a paper-lover. Were Mrs. Lippcott to forget to put a box of Kleenex in the car (but how could she forget this sacrosanct tissue that serves at once as handkerchief, napkin, and make-up remover?) he would be as unhappy as Pochet without his *Guide Michelin*.[2] One of the things that most amazed Lippcott during his latest stay in Paris was to see Parisians walking about with loaves of bread under their arms—without paper! For an asepticized and microbe-haunted American such a thing is simply unthinkable.

In his bathroom at the Statler Hotel in Washington, D.C., Pochet was struck speechless with admiration over the (paper) seat cover in the W.C. (Will I be forgiven for speaking of such things? After all, it did not concern me.)

wwwwwwwwwwwww

[1] A general verification of the organs which Americans undergo at regular intervals, and particularly after a trip to the Old World, notorious breeding-ground for germs.

[2] The first thing you notice on the rear seat of any American car is a blue Kleenex box. If you don't see it, it's because the manufacturer has already furnished the car with a built-in Kleenex box.

"Why do you say you're a failure, when you can pay my bills."

"This seat," read the guaranty accompanying the reserve supply of seat covers, "is perfectly sterilized and un- touched by human hand." Was it because of this admo- nition that the intimacy of the bathroom seemed to Pochet suddenly to have been invested with an unusual solem- nity?

You can imagine the daily torture that a trip to old Gaul represents for Lippcott. In his own country everything is wrapped up—the salt, the sugar, the meat, the bread, the fruit, the utensils, and even, in tiny cellophane envelopes, the postage stamps that the stamp machine distributes between little strips of cardboard. In one of the hotels we stayed at, the breakfast was delivered to us in a cardboard container, which was shoved through a hatchway at the bottom of the door. Martine finds "their" wrappings so wonderful that she claims she could spend hours admiring a package before opening it (annoying in the case of a breakfast). In the meantime the number of boxes she has already collected is so great that, if it keeps up, I shall leave here boxed and crated.

"But look, *chéri,* how it is all wrapped up!" she exclaimed, when my laundry came back to me at the hotel.

And true enough: my shirts were returned to me buried in a blue carton, enveloped in a sheet of white paper, swathed in blankets of tissue paper, beribboned with green paper bands, and stuffed with gray cardboard backing. (The only annoying thing—due no doubt to an excess of starch—was that the shirts themselves were as stiff as boards.)

Yes, the U.S.A. is the Realm of Wrapping Paper. On days when it rains, Lippcott with his plastic hat-cover, shoe covers, trouser covers, and raincoat seems to me to be perfectly packaged. And it's a fact that at nine o'clock of any morning in New York the men and women, looking cleaner and more neatly dressed than Latins in their Sunday best, seem to have just stepped out of their boxes.

For these paper-lovers the crowning day of the week is, quite naturally, the Sabbath. That day Cyrus and his family literally disappear behind mountains of paper (for the family: 26 pounds of Sunday newspaper). So much so that when I turned up unexpectedly at their place a couple of Sundays ago I couldn't see them at first. I keep wondering, indeed, if on Sundays it's the Americans that devour their papers or the papers that swallow them up.[3]

All this is disconcerting to Pochet. He had a prefabricated America in his head, and it was not at all the one he has encountered here. Every Frenchman knows—as Pochet used to know—that the average American is a man who:

[a] is awakened by soft music in his apartment on the fifty-first floor of a skyscraper, chews his first chewing-gum tablet, and has a brain storm while shaving;

---

[3] Be it noted, however, that in the land of paper, there is one thing you are never asked for: your papers. You can live and die in the United States without ever having to show an identity card.

[b] gets breakfast ready for the American divinity—his wife—while barely having time to think of his own;

[c] leaps into an express elevator and from there into his fluid-drive station wagon;

[d] is pursued by motorcycle cops after going through a red light, races a (siren-wailing) train, beats it to the railroad crossing and reaches the Exchange Mortgage Company on the dot of nine;

[e] climbs, floor by floor, all the echelons of the hierarchy, finally invading the scenic-view office of the company president, to whom he unfolds his brain storm and by whom he is warmly congratulated and given the management of the plant;

[f] bolts his lunch in a drugstore;

[g] returns home in the evening, dog-tired but victorious, and finds a note from the divinity informing him that, weary of always having to wait for him, she has taken the plane for Reno and is suing for divorce on the grounds of "mental cruelty";

[h] is ruined the next day by the crash of the Exchange Mortgage Company, but, still smiling, starts again from scratch as a simple workingman with Ford—the future is his.

In fact, nothing of the sort occurs. Lippcott never

chews gum (out of date, poor form) and never would he have the insane idea of racing through a red light.

Pochet had been told that the Americans were simple, frugal people. Yet the Lippcotts would think it an offense to offer him fruit for dessert. In the United States it is now almost impossible to buy a car of only one color, and Martine claims that American women have lovely little dresses, but that they can't resist adding a little *"kiki qui fiche tout par terre."*

Pochet was expecting to find feverish, hectic people, ceaselessly running around. Instead, he finds citizens who have mastered the art of hurrying slowly, who never run (at the Douglas Factory in Los Angeles signboards recommend: *Here we are in a hurry: do not run*) and who take their time thinking.

Back in France, Pochet had been told of ruthless gangsters and dead-end kids; but, instead, he finds people obeying a ritual of politeness infinitely more rigorous than in any country in Europe, even mine.

Nothing impresses Pochet more than to see thirty Americans packed in an elevator, as though moved by a single spring, simultaneously take off their hats, to salute the entrance of a girl on the twenty-fourth floor. But what intrigues him even more is the ritual of the dinner table and the mechanical ballet of knife and fork. For meat one must: (a) take the fork in the left hand and the knife in the right; (b) set down the knife on the edge of the plate and transfer the fork to the right hand, while the left hand goes under the table; jab and eat; (c) begin the same operation all over again for the next piece.

For Pochet, who couldn't tell you exactly where his knife and fork go when he is eating and who insists on guarding his plate to the left and the right of him with his two hands, this little game of cut-and-jab-and-jab-and-cut seems quite incompatible with the art of good eating.[4] When he expressed his surprise at finding American men and, particularly, American women eating with their left arms under the table, the Major told him that this custom dated from the days of the pioneers, who had to keep one hand on their Colts while eating.

~~~~~~~~~~~~~~~~~~~~

[4] In France it is considered poor manners not to keep one's wrists on the edge of the table while eating. This rule is particularly binding on the man, for if he keeps his hands in his lap, he is always suspected of trying to hold hands under the table with the lady seated to the left or right of him.

Chapter 15

[P.D.]

COCKTAIL PARTY

Americans, who leave very little to chance since chance
led to the discovery of their country, have in recent times
perfected, among other things, a school for dogs and phono-
graph records for parakeets.

I won't say much about the school for *comme-il-faut*
dogs, intended not only to train and restrain dogs in polite
society (innate qualities in the British dog, Major Thompson assures us), but also to teach them to walk in a
straight line in the street (without tugging on the leash),

to bark correctly, and to wear tuxedos.[1] But I would like to say something, on the other hand, about the unsuspected advantages to be derived from parakeet records—advantages of less benefit to the parakeets themselves than to people who have just arrived in the United States.

When Cyrus B. Lippcott told me that he trained his parakeet, Jasper, with the aid of a record, I only half believed him, and I rushed over to a record-shop on Broadway, privately persuaded that they were going to laugh in my face. This the salesman did, not to tell me it was a joke, but because my request seemed to him as preposterous as if I had asked for a concerto for piano and orchestra without naming the composer.

~~~~~~~~~~~~~~~~~~~~~

[1] It should be noted that in treeless cities the education of dogs must be particularly thorough. The school year for dogs corresponds to that for children (September–June). At the end of a six-month "obedience class" the good student-dog receives a diploma complete with gold seal and red ribbon. The poor students are sent out of the city and entrusted to friends in the country. The tuxedo is only one of many items in the wardrobe of the fashionable Yankee dog, which also includes camel's-hair coats, charming little hats, and brightly colored raincoats. It should be added that the standard of (dog) living is very high in New York, where a prize is offered annually for the *Most Elegant Dog*, where dogs are fed scientific diets, have their own bar (in marble) on Fifth Avenue, their own visiting-cards, and their own hairdressers. There you will look in vain for one of those unkempt mongrels with no fixed address which swarm over the Old Continent.

"There are twenty-five of them," he said to me. "Which do you want?"

I am struck by the prodigious way the parrot side of my nature has developed in the few days I have been in the United States. By dint of hearing the same expressions repeated morning, noon, and night, you end up unconsciously using them yourself. What are they? To reply to this question I spent a whole day going around with a pocket tape-recorder (of which there are many models in the U.S.A.). In the evening I added up the expressions most frequently recorded. Without even mentioning the obvious—"Glad to meet you" . . . "Hope to see you again" —I cannot, for reasons of space, make a complete listing here of the fifty-odd passwords that enable one to get by in the United States (*"lovely, darling, relax, check! Nuts! O.K.! wonderful! fine, fabulous, gorgeous,* etc.).

How does a foreigner go about memorizing and correctly pronouncing this pocket vocabulary?

Cyrus Lippcott put me on the right track by recommending the method used by parakeets. What a mass of time you save! If you tried to collect the umpteen clichés of the American language all by yourself, you would lose precious hours and risk going off your rocker. The parakeet record, on the other hand, faithfully reproduces all the key phrases, murmured ten times over by a charming feminine voice, suave but articulate. Besides, a parakeet's education is a thousand times more rapid than a schoolboy's. A parakeet must be very quick on the uptake and get into the swim of things straight away, so as not to get off just any old remark in society. There's no point wasting years teaching him the reactions of sunflowers or the role of Pericles in antiquity. He can be taught what to say in a living-room in the very first (record) class, *Social Contacts.*

That is why, having become a parrot myself, I learned more in one parakeet lesson (under the direction of Allen B. Jacobs—78 rpm.) than in a month of tape-recordings. And at the beginning of the second year class, suitable for a parakeet of forty-three—just my age—I had already reached *Romantic Phrases*, with expressions such as: *Hi babe!* [2] *Hello sweetheart! Gosh! You're cute! How about a date?*

At the end of eight days of training, I was ready. I was ready for anything in the American world. I was

---

[2] Masters in the art of decontraction, Americans are also unsurpassed in matters of contraction. *Hi!* is the final contraction of *How are you?* which was *Hi-ya*, before being finally reduced to two letters. Like the schoolboys in France, Americans love to shorten words and, above all, names. In a country where Dwight D. Eisenhower becomes "Ike," and Cyrus B. Lippcott "Cy," Montesquieu would become "Monti" or "TQ."

Facsimile of the record cover for Romantic Phrases. *Though designed for parakeets, it proved invaluable to the author.*

ready, above all, to face that redoubtable institution: the cocktail party.

The American colonists who came to this country fifty or more years ago craved solitude and the wide-open spaces; they crossed an ocean to free themselves from the pomp and circumstance of the Old World. But their descendants now feel a daily need to crowd themselves into overheated rooms where, unable to breathe or to hear each other, they sacrifice solitude to the most sacred of all rites: the cocktail.

An American cocktail party is organized in honor of anyone and anything: a reception for a Duchess, the arrival of a writer, the visit of a cousin from Detroit. It allows you to meet a great number of people with whom it is quite naturally impossible to talk, but whom you can arrange to meet some other day. On that day your new acquaintance, who would think it disobliging to receive you alone, will ask over a few friends in your honor to make it a "party." This is a vicious circle no one seems anxious to escape from.

Somewhat similar to the Parisian cocktail party, though infinitely more frequent, more ritualistic, and more formal, the American cocktail party is utterly unlike the London variety: one more difference between these two countries. English life is nothing but a huge masquerade ball in which the participants contrive to conceal their feelings, their addresses, their hobbies, their incomes, their decorations, their sorrows, their talents, their achievements, and even their names. (At a London cocktail party it's almost impossible to know just whom you are dealing with.)

America, on the other hand, is a huge glass house where everything is advertised in black and white: success, financial status, hobbies, and, above all, names. Our friend Cyrus gets a great kick out of conventions. He can prance around, like a child at a summer camp, with his name (and state) printed in big letters on the card in his buttonhole. Besides, to avoid all error, it is quite common for the hostess to preface an introduction with a few vital statistics: "Allow me to introduce the well-known champion who ran the 220 in 20 and 2/10 seconds, Mr. Melvin Sam Holgerson."

And now here is the (high fidelity) tape-recording of a cocktail party held at 696 Fifth Avenue, New York, between 5.30 and 7.00 P.M. There were, as you will notice, a few French people in the room to add to the confusion:

"Glad to meet you! . . . Isn't that cute! . . . Yes, but watch out: New York isn't America. You should go out West. May I introduce Mr. Thaddeus Apfelbaum, of Apfelbaum, Birbenstock, and Company. . . . Pleased to meet you! . . . If you go to Los Angeles, don't fail to look up the DeWitte Clintons—delightful people—they know everybody; I'll give you a note for them. Hope to see you again. . . . *Ce n'est pas un pays; c'est un continent;*

prenez leurs trains, eh bien vous passez la journée dans le train, vous êtes aux Etats Unis. Vous repassez la nuit, vous êtes toujours . . . Well, I'll tell you now: in three years it'll be all over; she married him only for his money. . . . They're a bunch of snobs! . . . Let me introduce Mrs. Mildred McPherson of the Columbia Broadcasting System. . . . Don't you think there's a touch of Farouk in him? . . . If you go to Chicago, don't fail to look up the Fergusons; they'll give you a royal welcome—they know everybody. I'm going to give you a note. . . . *Non, ils ne sont pas bêtes; ce sont de grands enfants. . . . Vous avez beau dire, nous pourrions prendre modèle sur eux pour beaucoup de choses, tenez leurs douches par exemple, eh bien, ce matin, vous ne le croirez pas, Alfred.* . . . You're welcome! . . . Have you ever thought seriously about the Negro problem? . . . Well, I don't find her so good looking. It'll last six months. . . . You must go to Las Vegas! . . . You know what I'd do if I were you? I'd hire a car. . . . Glad to meet you! . . . If you were American, you'd speak differently. . . . You know she comes from a very good family, her mother's a Cabot. . . . Hi! Paree, ah! Paree! Lovely city! *Oui, mais Mendès n'a pas voulu, voilà.* . . . You should go to San Francisco. . . . Relax! . . . I thought they were divorced? . . . If I were in your place, I'd take a bus—you can really get to know people. . . .

The Major at an American cocktail party.

Gorgeous! I thought they were in Mexico. I give them just six months. . . . I never would've believed it of her. . . . Come back next year and we'll talk it over again. . . . D'you realize you're on the same latitude as Madrid? . . . *Mais voyons! Ils sont bien plus près des Russes que vous ne le pensez.* . . . If you haven't seen Kansas City, you haven't seen anything. . . . The Chinese won't co-operate, you'll see. . . . Pleased to meet you. . . . Is it really true that France has gone Communist? . . . What about a date? *Au fond, c'est très province, quoi? Mais New York, ma chère, c'est Angoulême, vous verrez:* ANGOULÊME! . . . *Leurs robes du soir sont d'un kiki!* . . . *Oui, mais ils font de gentilles robes de sport* . . . Bulganin will never make it. . . . They're very strong. . . . They told me it stank. . . . To really get to know us, you have to live in the Middle West. You should go to Oklahoma. No, to Sioux City! Yes sir, Sioux City! . . . *Ils vont voir le psychanalyste pour un oui ou pour un non.* . . . *Les enfants sont rois.* . . . It's better in orlon. . . . If you go to Seattle, I'll give you a note for the Chandlers; they know everybody. . . . Now when you're up against the problem of 300 million people. . . . If you haven't seen Dallas, you haven't seen anything. . . . They arrived yesterday. . . . The Duke is here. . . . They left this morning. . . . *Ce que je trouve épatant c'est leurs ice-creams! Vous savez qu'ils font du vin?* . . . *On aura tout bu!* . . . He's with his wife? . . . We're going tomorrow. . . . How long are you staying? . . . If you go to Pittsburgh be sure to look up Coolidge Junior, the old man has gone to pot, it's the nephew who really runs the show. . . . But just take the train, that's all. . . . The nice thing about it is that you don't even have to dry the dishes. . . . She killed him all right. . . . A word of advice: take the plane. . . ."

When I was alone again in the street, my befuddled brain was a heaving mass of faces, formulas, and figures. The bus or the train? Sioux City or Baltimore? I had to look up the DeWitte Clintons, and the MacClutches, and the Pattersons.

The Major had disappeared. The Pochets had gone off to the Lippcotts'. It was raining. I suddenly felt very much alone, as one can only be in a city of eight million isolated souls that eight hundred parties have momentarily brought together.

Chapter 16

[P . D .]

THE ART OF SLEEPING
WITH YOUR EYES OPEN

The most painful thing in life is not being bored. It's being compelled to pretend you're having a good time.

Take for example those dinner parties—those terrible dinner parties where you must talk, where you must scintillate. Where you must know who's who, what to say to whom, how to reply to what. On your neighbor's plate there's a little place card. Leaning over casually you try to decipher the name of—Wannamaker-Baxter. You say to yourself: "That's petroleum." And it turns out to be municipal gas. All the conversational crochet-work must be done over. Ah! Those dinners where you must give your opinion on the Pentagon, Eisenhower, Poujade, Suez, and China!

What can one do about it?

Well, the Americans have given me the answer to the problem. In a country where a man who can't live in public is banned by society, it was only normal that they should one day discover a way of allowing people to sleep upright while appearing wide-awake.

Long experience has taught me that boredom begins with the feet. When you're gay, when you're relaxed, you don't think of your feet. You put them anywhere, any old how. You can even scratch them. It's marvelous! But at dinner parties, or, at any rate, those that I am thinking of here, your feet are the first to start puffing with boredom. By a kind of parallel action your back begins to sag, your head nods, your eyelids droop. Deafened by the uproar, the noise of dishes and the dishing out of noise ("You're not taking a second helping? It's all there is, you know.") harassed by shrill voices ("Have you been going out a lot lately? And how's the skiing?") you feel an invincible torpor steal over you. Softly settling into a state of semi-consciousness, you dream of that distant land, so close yet inaccessible—that El Dorado where you can pull off your tie, walk barefoot on the carpet, and bury your nose in a sofa—home. Oh! at nine in the evening how far away midnight seems! You will have to cross the Urals, span Siberia, argue with Mao Tse-tung, give your opinion on Prince

Rainier, and lose yourself in a labyrinth of *liaisons* before you can make a getaway.

Not long ago at a dinner in Washington, a gentleman was explaining how twenty years ago he had bought a lemonade from Grace Kelly on the beach at Atlantic City. How I would have enjoyed tasting a bit of it myself, but my neighbor had me backed up against Greenland.

"Now d'you really think we can put up with a thing like that?" he asked me.

"Of course not!" I said.

"Yes, and it's the same with Madagascar," he went on, and, dragging me away from Grace Kelly, he dumped me in Tananarive.

Until recently—that is, before getting Cyrus B. Lippcott's advice—I used to employ a pretty primitive method, effective but sometimes dangerous, to cope with such situations. I just let myself be put to sleep gradually by my neighbor. Why talk? He talks about everything so well! Yes, you've guessed it. He's one of those staggering men who go from Montherlant to Mollet by way of the White House, with a passing reference or two to NATO and UNESCO.

There's only one thing to do with this kind of man. Wind him up again, like a watch—the most convenient wind-up-again words being: "You're dead right!" or else

"Oh, absolutely!" A "You really think so?" a simple "Oh, come now!" or an "In my opinion, it's unlikely!" can also restart the express. If you want to hedge a little, an "I don't think I'd go quite as far as that, but . . ." can be risky, whereas a simple "Oh! but how true!" will put the locomotive-man back on the rails and set him off again. You can eat your chicken in peace.

There's only one trouble with this method: you suddenly notice that something isn't functioning. The train has stopped. You realize that a question has been put to you and that a mere grunt of agreement won't do; a precise answer is expected. You've just said: "In my opinion, it's unlikely!" thinking that you've been following the drift of the conversation, and only too late do you realize that he asked you if you were a bachelor!

This kind of catastrophe occurred all the more frequently during my first weeks in the United States, because of the novelty of the cacophonic babble I found myself submerged in. At a dinner in Boston, I had done quite a bit of mileage on "Yes and no's" and "No doubt's," and had just come out with an emphatic: "I never would have thought it!" when I realized that I had been asked if I was born in Paris. I was mortified.

It was after this misadventure that Cyrus B. Lippcott recommended the use of some miraculous glasses that keep you from ever giving others the impression that you're bored. These glasses, called *Refuge-Specs,* patented and manufactured by the H. Gardner Company of Ossining (N.Y.), were destined to change my life. Put on a pair and there is no further need of saying a single word, so much do they give your partner the impression that you are drinking in his words. You can simply go to sleep while seeming to be the most captivated listener in the world.

These glasses, as you may have guessed, have eyes of their own, eyes painted on, together with eyelids and eyebrows. It would be an understatement to describe them as matching reality, since they far surpass it. Two tiny holes in the middle of the metal lenses on the same level as your pupils enable you to cast an occasional glance at the situation.

"Nap politely, yet look alert—at the opera, at conferences, or at dinner parties," reads the card that comes with them. You can, furthermore, choose the particular model best suited to your complexion. "Select the suitable personality," the notice continues, establishing three "basic personalities": (a) *cool, intellectual;* (b) *eager beaver;* (c) *shy, demure.*

Each of the three models has its particular advantages. To sleep politely at the theater or during lectures, I would particularly recommend the "cool, intellectual" model. On the other hand, the "eager beaver"—two wide-open and incredibly avid eyes—enabled me to weather a lengthy harangue on the International Monetary Fund which would otherwise have completely ossified me.

In my opinion, the best solution is to arm yourself with all three pairs at once, since your partner may be surprised at being confronted by such a fixed stare for a long period of time. If you have three pairs you can take advantage of one of those moments when men take off their glasses to rub their eyelids (a gesture well thought of among big industrialists, businessmen, and even intellectuals) and, with a negligent gesture, exchange an *eager beaver* for a *shy, demure*.

These "wide-open eye" spectacles are, all things considered, just one of the 1,001 answers to the "Hows" that American experts keep churning out for the book trade— from *How to make friends* and *How to live with yourself* to *How to buy and sell* and *How to win your wife's confidence.*

There is not a "How" that escapes the sagacity of these experts. The spectacular reply to the question: "How to sleep while seeming awake?" only goes to prove that in a country where people knock themselves out to have a good time, there's sometimes a touch of boredom in the air.

Just spend a few days in a typical American small town like Decatur (Alabama)—which is strangely like Du-Quoin (Illinois) or Coeur d'Alene (Idaho)—with its Main Street, its First National Bank (neo-Greco façade), its red brick schoolhouse, its Woman's Club, its Liggett's Drug Store, its town hall, its supermarket, and its Methodist Church, and you'll realize that life in the U.S.A. is not always a picnic.

This helps to explain the success of lectures in this country, particularly foreign lectures—the word of a visitor from afar always being invested with a special prestige. If a Norwegian, or an Englishman, or a Frenchman turns up one night in Des Moines (Iowa), he is sure to pack the lecture hall. Whether he's an explorer, missionary, industrialist, deep-sea diver, writer, or bicycle racer, he represents for the local Woman's Club a topic of conversation, an excuse for going out, a change from TV or the movies.

The subject matters very little, as is proved by this true story. One of Major Thompson's fellow countrymen was some years ago vegetating in the United States, whither the hazards of existence had brought him. Like many another, he was casting around for an idea that would bring him success in the New World. One day a Colonel Bodley (another of the Major's countrymen and,

Psychopanorama of

American small town.

like him, an ex-Indian army officer), who lives near Boston, advised his compatriot, who had a certain gift of speech, to take up lecturing.

"All right. But about what?"

"Any old thing," cried the Colonel. And then, as they were walking past a church, he said: "Here, why don't you talk about bells?"

"Bells? But . . . I don't know a blessed thing about bells!"

"More's the reason! Bone up on the subject and then talk about what you've learned."

The Colonel's friend followed his advice and delved into the *Encyclopedia Britannica.* One hour later he already knew more about bells than you, I, or any American. He quickly realized that there was a tremendous amount to be said about bells, bell-ringers, handbells, and belfries, from the first Chinese bell to Big Ben, via jingle-bells, bluebells, and dumbbells. Today he could write a *How to* book entitled *How to succeed in life thanks to bells.* For it's thanks to bells that this man is now making a small fortune in the U.S.A. With his one lecture, for which he was first paid $15, and now gets $300, he goes from town to town, year in year out, earning a good $10,000 a year. Not bad for bells!

It should be noted that as a subject bells present certain advantages. You can always make a personal allusion to the bell of the locality where you are speaking, for there is bound to be at least one bell in a town, even if it's only the bell of a passing train.

"It gives me particular pleasure," the lecturer assures his audience, "to speak to you tonight about bells, for your church (or town-hall or fire-engine) bell has a quite unique ring. . . ."

With one stroke he has won the sympathy of the ladies of the Women's Club, who form the backbone of American audiences and are ever eager to learn something about anything. I can't guarantee, of course, that there won't be a few recalcitrant husbands in the audience who have been dragged along by their wives. Some of them may even pull out their *Refuge-Specs,* but no matter! For at least eight days in Pascagoula (Mississippi) everyone will be talking about bells. They make, shall we say, a "nice conversation piece."

Chapter 17

[P . D .]

AMERICA IN A NUTSHELL

When I got back to Paris from the United States, I told my editor: "All things considered, I think I can sum up America in a phrase."

Despite the importance of this news, he didn't look at all happy. Concision may be a precious literary quality, but the writer who returns from a 15,000-mile trip to tell his editor that he can wrap it all up in three lines is looked upon with a jaundiced eye. And even though I had to travel all the way to Salt Lake City (Utah)—that is, a good 6,000 miles from the Eiffel Tower—to pick up this phrase, it seemed really a bit steep to my editor. "You can't do this to me," he said, "you'd better go right back."

I therefore reimbursed my publishers by coughing up something like 80,000 extra words, but my opinion hasn't changed. All America is still summed up for me in the phrase I heard one morning at the Utah Hotel in Salt Lake City. I had asked to be awakened at 7.00 A.M. On the stroke of seven the telephone rang. And over the wire came the divine voice of the American telephone girl, a voice formed at the Voice School before the mirror of amiability (three months for a degree), a voice full of sex appeal, sweetness, and precision:

"Good morning, Mister Denainos! It's seven o'clock! I hope you enjoyed your sleep! Weather's clear and temperature 36 degrees Fahrenheit. Thank you!"

These twenty-two words are America in a nutshell. First of all, my name! Oh, adorable switchboard operator, how well you learned to say my name! Up there in that bleak room on the fourteenth floor of a Midwest hotel, where I was alone with a black Bible, the telephone directory, and the distant wailing of the locomotives of the Western Pacific, your beautifully modulated voice came through the liquid dawn, leaving a trail of bell-like echoes ringing in my ears: ". . . ning! . . . nos! . . . clock! . . . joy! . . . nice! . . . kyou!" You spoke the same words to

M. Pochet, and he, too, no longer felt alone in the land of the Mormons. Hospitable America smiled at him through your voice: you graciously invited him to get up and live.

"*Good morning, Mister Pochett!*"

That morning, amid 166 million citizens, in this nation of pioneer conquests and booms and busts, you gave him strength by uttering his name. In Salt Lake City Pochet isn't just anybody; he's M. Pochet, and you know that he's French, that he likes *Châteaubriants* and the Folies-Bergère, that he has the *Légion d'Honneur* and a bit of the Eiffel Tower about him.

Americans cultivate names as we Frenchmen cultivate *petit pois*. No sooner does Pochet check in at a hotel and register than the manager, who can read upside down, catches his name—the name that will never leave him: "Good morning, Mister Pochett. . . . You're welcome, Mister Pochett!" He could just as well be called Mavrogordato or De Stumpf-Quichelier; the reflex would be the same. Americans are name-catchers, and those whose job it is to specialize in "public relations" possess a particular aptitude for this kind of sport. They catch the most-forbidding names with the agility of a butterfly catcher, promptly pinion it in their memories, mount it, and offer it back to you, carefully preserved and framed, as though it were one of their most cherished specimens.[1]

One of the great teachers of the American way of life, Mr. Dale Carnegie, lays great stress on the importance of names in his book *How To Win Friends and Influence People*. He cites revealing cases of people who have succeeded in life simply because they could pronounce names pleasantly with a smile, thus creating a climate of confidence.

In the plane the TWA Air Hostess, who has fifty-five passengers to take care of, asks Pochet—whom she didn't know ten minutes earlier and may never see again in her life—"Would you like some coffee, Mr. Pochett?" She thus gives him the comforting sensation of remaining M. Pochet even 18,000 feet above Death Valley and lost in the immensity of a continent where barely a hundred years ago the dog-eating redskins smoked their peace-pipes by the bodies of their scalped victims. She caresses him with the soft name of Pochet; she pulls him from the

[1] In America when you apply for a ticket to Miami at the airlines office, you don't address yourself to just anybody, but (as the brass plaque on his desk indicates) to Mr. Pegram, and at the post office it's Mr. Murchison who gives you a fifteen-cent stamp.

abyss of anonymity; she gives him a gentle push along the road to fame.

"I hope you enjoyed your sleep."

Oh, telephone girl of my dreams, how soft your voice sounds when it says *"enjoy!"* Lovely voice . . . I would almost ask you to come on up, but no! that wouldn't be proper, that would be un-American. Yes, I enjoyed my sleep. Here people *enjoy* everything—a good night's sleep, a good drive, a good whisky, a good vacation, a good party, a good bed.[2]

Your attentiveness touches me. You are the voice of America, the voice of this Realm of Friendliness, where all day long the air rings with "Glad to meet you" and "You're welcome."

All over the world, of course, people tell you they're happy to meet you. But Americans really seem to mean it. When we French say *"très heureux,"* we might just as well say *"condoléances"* or *"A bientôt."*

We aren't likely to be happy, for we already know enough people as it is. But in the United States it's just

⁓⁓⁓⁓⁓⁓⁓⁓⁓⁓

[2] A pamphlet that was put out during the war for the benefit of the members of the Women's Army Corps advised them, if importuned in enemy or occupied territory by over-enterprising men: "Just relax and enjoy it!"

the opposite. People are delighted to get to know you; they seem to have been waiting for this blessed moment for years. Two bright eyes plunge into yours, a smile lights up the face of the newcomer, and a hearty handshake seals the exalted moment: "Glad to meet you!"

Everyone must partake of this spirit of general affability. It's un-American to pull a long face, not to smile at the new day, at the person you meet, at the task awaiting you. Everywhere posters remind you: "Keep smiling!" [3] You must show a smile all your life, right up to your dying gasp—and even after since post-mortem make-up artists undertake, by an ultimate contraction of the zygomatics, to fix it for eternity.

The poorly trained foreigner sometimes succumbs to this avalanche of friendliness. And it is also true that in this game of smiles and affability American men wear themselves out faster than women.

"The whole question," Major Thompson said to me, "boils down to this: whether it's better to live to a ripe old age among disagreeable people or to die young among the most hospitable people on earth."

~~~~~~~~~~~~~~~~

[3] Even American dogs are not exempt. A couple of *Equanil* pills, a new product made for the canine world, are guaranteed within forty-eight hours to bring a smile to the surliest bulldog. For further details, consult the dog psychiatrist in your neighborhood.

". . . . and temperature 36 degrees Fahrenheit. Thank you!"

This was perhaps what most amazed Pochet. For a fleeting moment he must have imagined the look that would come over the night porter's face at the Hotel de la Gare at Poitiers if he was asked to awaken Pochet in the morning with a question about his sleep and a report on the temperature outside. Here in the United States they not only ask nothing of you, but they give you everything, adding a "Thank you" at the end.[4]

And what precision! The voice did not say: "There's a nip in the air!" or "It's chilly outside; better dress warmly." No, it said: "36 degrees Fahrenheit." In Amer-

~~~~~~~~~~~~~~~~~~

[4] This "Thank you," pronounced with a markedly rising inflection by American feminine voices, is used on all sorts of occasions—when there is no need to say "thank you" at all. It can sometimes be disconcerting. When you tell a French woman that she has the loveliest eyes in the world, she smiles, says nothing or else: *"Vous êtes fou!"* and occasionally lets herself be kissed. When you tell an English woman that she has the loveliest eyes in the world, she stops you, saying: "Don't be silly!" When you tell an American woman that she has the loveliest eyes in the world, she says: "Thank you," as though you had just passed her the salt. Things stay where they are until the next move is made; it's the rule of the game. And she will say "thank you" in exactly the same tone in reply to "Your dress is lovely" or "I like your handwriting."

ica a sentence isn't really a sentence unless there's at least one figure in it.

M. Pochet is a grown boy: he knows what he must do when the thermometer reads 36 degrees so he won't get a sore throat—and bring it back to Madame, thanks!

"Thank you very much!" he himself replied to the switchboard operator, already feeling himself to be part of this land of courteous service, where even the cigarette machines are taught to say "thank you." "Thanks for buying me," says the wrapper on the chocolate bar. "Thanks" says the voice of the new mechanical robot in the U. S. Post Offices when you buy a stamp off him.

The American "thank you" is not just a word; it can also become a function. What are you? "I am a thanker." In the U.S.A. there are *thankers* whose job it is to thank others. During the war when blood donors used to line up at Red Cross plasma centers, they would be met at the exit by a lady-thanker, a lady with a monthly-remunerated smile who thanked them for co-operating in the war effort. They had smilingly obeyed the first law of America—co-operation.

Chapter 18

[W . M . T .]

THE PRAYING MANTIS
or
The Secret of American Womanhood [1]

I already know what my good friend Daninos is going to say; he is going to say that I care more about animals than about human beings. It's true, of course, that as a good Englishman, I am a bit more attached to the former than the latter. But, good heavens! is it my fault if I have probed the secret of American womanhood by way of the American heifer? And can I honestly be blamed for being so struck, not to say shocked, by the American woman's omnipotence that I have come to liken her to a praying mantis

wwwwwwwwwwwwww

[1] Major Thompson has expressed a desire to say a few words about American women. I gladly yield the pen to him once more. He was doubtless afraid that I might treat the subject properly. (P.D.)

who devours three or four husbands in a lifetime and replenishes herself on insurance policies and alimonies?

I shall, no doubt, be accused of being prone to exaggeration in this field, since I belong to a nation where man is king. But even Pochet is of much the same opinion. One hundred years ago the United States seemed to be a land of widowers; today it seems to him the greatest boardinghouse for widows in the world. He can't get over meeting so many women who speak gaily of their third or fourth husbands.

One day when Pochet was visiting a famous Fifth Avenue jewelry store in search of a *petite quelque chose* for his wife to "mark" the trip by, the salesman said to him: "We never ask a customer: 'How is your husband?' He's sure to be either dead or divorced. Besides, we never have men coming into our store; it's the women who do all the buying. The kind of slick seducer who has a diamond clip delivered to Baroness So-and-So in the hope of obtaining her favors is a strictly Latin type; here men play it safe."

As far as I'm concerned, my mind is made up. American men use up a shocking amount of their strength in work, mostly to assure the well-being of the voracious mantes, who hold them in a state closely akin to slavery. Just take poor old Cyrus B. Lippcott. From the moment he gets up to prepare breakfast for his divinity until he goes to bed at night (after taking in the TV program his wife has chosen) he hardly has an instant of peace and quiet. He no sooner buys the latest-model refrigerator or the latest "hi-fi" record-player than his wife starts talking of the even more up-to-date one that the Fergusons have. And so the poor fellow develops another complex!

On the boat coming back from their vacation in Europe, Mrs. Lippcott was already telling Cyrus of her plans for "doing" the Caribbean the next year. And have you ever listened to the way American wives complain that their husbands come home exhausted from the office and think only of going to bed, instead of wanting to "go places and do something?" Really, these wives have deplorable habits. They ought to be disciplined!

But for that I suppose we shall have to wait a goodish time. In the meantime, I don't think I've ever seen anyone look more startled than the after-dinner company at one of those venerable Beacon Street houses in Boston. And all because, as I was settling into a comfortable armchair, I asked Martine if she wouldn't mind fetching my pipe, which I had left in my raincoat. Mrs. O'Neil, our Boston hostess, couldn't believe her ears, nor could Mrs. Bainbridge or the Cabots, her guests. Why, the idea of it! Fancy asking your wife to leave the drawing-room and

Major Thompson, followed by Mrs. Bruce Patterson, surprising his old comrade-in-arms, "The Lion of the Ardennes" (Colonel Bruce R. Patterson), now returned to the joys of civilian life.

go fetch your pipe! An unheard of enormity in the United States, even in the most English of cities. And to think that Martine complied with a smile! That was the last straw! I had stood the world on its head!

Even Pochet has been bothered by all this, though he may by now have grown accustomed to the manners of a country where a man anticipates a woman's slightest wish. There's something automatic, almost ritualistic about the way American men get up the moment a woman walks in or out of a drawing-room, the way they help a lady into her chair at the dinner table, and the way they rush to carry her coat, bag, packages, and umbrella as soon as, and often before, she shows the slightest sign of fatigue.

By Jove! I don't call it politeness. I call it subservience. Never would an Englishman think of being reduced to the status of porter.

Mme Pochet, however, finds this a blissful state of affairs: "They are *so* much more polite than our men, *n'est-ce-pas?*" she said to Martine, who, of course, agreed.

I must say that Pochet since his sojourn in the United States has never been more attentive. Now, he never drives anywhere to pick up his wife without getting out to open the door for her. And he always thinks of the little push to be given her chair when she sits down at table.

"On m'a changé mon Alfred!" she says.

Well, Pochet can be changed. But not I!

Now my touchy friend Daninos has objected that women all over the world have a bit of the praying mantis in them. He has also pointed out that the working conditions in the United States are better than anywhere else. All this perplexed me to the point of wondering if I were not barking up the wrong tree. Still, there is one undeniable fact: in this hemisphere, between the twenty-fifth and the forty-ninth parallels, man wears himself out much more quickly than woman. Was the answer to this damnable riddle to be found, then, in purely geographic causes?

It was finally an Iowa cattle-raiser, a Mr. Clarence McKinley, who let me in on a secret when I was visiting his ranch near Council Bluffs. I am a trifle embarassed at having to divulge all this to the general public, but I feel duty bound to do so.

I know that highly responsible experts have made valuable statistical studies of the behavior of the American male, and yet through a study of the American cow I think I have gone almost as far as they.[2] Clarence McKinley offered me the explanation: whereas female cattle, and

ᴡᴡᴡᴡᴡᴡᴡᴡᴡᴡᴡ

[2] Past master of the art of understatement, the Major means "much further." (P.D.)

in general all domestic female animals, imported into the United States[3] develop with growing strength, the males begin to wilt after a few years and rapidly lose their reproductive powers. Breeders of thoroughbred horses and pedigree cattle must, therefore, frequently replenish their stock of stallions and bulls (particularly, I feel bound to add, with Aberdeen Anguses, Durhams, and Guernseys!—I can already hear Daninos exclaiming that I'm so insufferably proud of the supremacy of these splendid British beasts).

Be that as it may, it seems that this physical law applies with equal rigor to American men. Whereas the hen-pecked male is finally eliminated in the quarter-finals, the female reaches the finals more robust than ever. She wields authority with masculine dynamism and becomes ever more avid for action, reforms, parties, discussions, trips. At twenty she enters the age of glamour, the world of cover-girls. And if you read only the popular magazines, you'd end up wondering if there were any women over twenty-five in this country.[4] But the moment she finds

ᴡᴡᴡᴡᴡᴡᴡᴡᴡᴡᴡᴡᴡ

[3] The first colonists found some wild dogs and pigeons on hand, but North America's only contribution to domestic animal life was the turkey.

[4] It is curious to note that a woman's "ideal age" varies according to a regular progression from east to west across the globe. In America a woman reaches her physical prime from 18 to 25; in England from

herself condemned by the canons of feminine beauty, the mantis takes a second lease on life. Her youth is dead? Life begins at forty. This is the age at which millions of Mrs. Lippcotts, haunted by the thought of their vanished youths, close ranks and take in hand the country's moral, religious, educational, artistic, and social activities.

Mrs. Lippcott herself belongs to a good dozen associations: the Woman's Christian Temperance Union, the local Knitting Club (weekly meetings from 3.00 to 4.00 P.M. on Fridays), the Schenectady League of Optimists, the Daughters of the American Revolution, the Sewing Circle, the Board of Advisors for the *Social Register,* the Baptist Women's Club, the T.T.K.,[5] to say nothing of golf clubs or bowling clubs.

I suppose there are no more easeful moments in Mrs. Lippcott's life than those gatherings where a good hundred snappily dressed, chattering, energetic women between fifty and sixty congregate to hear their president call them "girls," as though they were sixteen-year-olds:

25 to 30; in France from 28 to 40. It is true, of course, that older people in the U.S.A. enjoy a second youth. Sixty-year-old women wear dresses fit for young girls and have at their disposal the most formidable arsenal of rejuvenating weapons in the world.

[5] *Truth Through Knowledge,* under whose auspices periodic meetings are held where lady members can listen to an account of a cruise or a mountain-climbing expedition while sewing or making pastry.

"Now, girls, let's come to order!" today's agenda being Mrs. Merrimack's trip to Kenya, juvenile delinquency, the influence of Chippendale on American furniture, or the organization of a league to combat the erection of nude statues.[6]

In my travels across the United States I have been struck by the omnipresence of Mrs. Lippcott in my audiences. Every lecturer must have been struck by the same thing. You see, I set out to give a round of lectures on the Indian Royal Tiger (*felis elongatus*), and before I was through, I no longer saw America as the land of skyscrapers, drugstores, ice creams, Hollywood, the Pentagon, and supermarkets; its symbol for me became the faces of three ladies, those three sexagenarian ladies, chirping like sparrows, who were on hand to meet me at the train or the

wwwwwwwwwwwww

[6] The reference is to the charming statue of a bacchante which the sculptor Frederic MacMonnies made in Paris and which the French government ordered a copy of for the Luxembourg Museum. It was originally intended to grace the court of Boston's Public Library; but the nudity of the dancing nymph, holding a child in one hand with a bunch of grapes in the other, was too shocking for New England's puritan society, which, while not outlawing the pleasures of the flesh, forbids one to enjoy them. A meeting of the Patriotic Temperance League finally voted for a resolution condemning this statue as "an insult to the virtuous sentiments of Massachusetts' capital city" and requesting that "this unmentionable thing" be destroyed. The unfortunate bacchante finally found a haven in New York's Metropolitan Museum. (P.D.)

"Look, Harry, what a disgrace! Treating a woman like that!
It's high time these people got civilized!"

airport in Des Moines and Omaha, Sioux City and Baltimore, Denver and Albuquerque—the president, the vice-
president and the secretary of the Women's Club.

Everywhere they had the same tidy, spruce, carefully made-up faces. Everywhere there were the same welcoming smiles, the same sparkling teeth: "So glad to
meet you, Major!" Everywhere there were the same rose-
pink strass-spangled dresses, the same blue satin toques
with white petals, the same jingling bracelets. Everywhere
they handed me the same little golden book to be signed.
And everywhere they apologized for their husbands, who
would have just loved to come, but unfortunately couldn't
make it, either because they were held up at the office, or
because they were dead.

I haven't a doubt any more that it is these three ladies, reproduced in hundreds of thousands of samples,
who really govern the United States. A strange vision indeed for my astonished English eye! But I'm not at all sure
that it isn't a vision that faithfully mirrors reality in this
matriarchy where Women's Clubs have more influence on
the White House than do the alcohol distillers on the
French Chamber of Deputies.[7]

wwwwwwwwwww

[7] This is to say nothing of certain states, such as Vermont, where
the inhabitants, who pride themselves on their origins, first ask of a new-

comer: "Who was his mother?" as though the father didn't count. The matriarchal tendency in the United States goes back to the dim past. Among the Hopi Indians, who live two hundred miles from the Grand Canyon, on the plateau tops of desolate mountains, the matriarchal system is still all-powerful. The house is the woman's property, and once a man is married, he goes to work on land belonging to his wife.

Chapter 19

[w . m . t .]

THE PURSUIT OF HAPPINESS

Every time our friend Cyrus B. Lippcott gets a chance to go to a football game and to recapture that "old college spirit" he does so with irrepressible exuberance. He sits down joyfully in the graduate section of the grandstand among his classmates of 1920 and exchanges boisterous salutations: "Hello, Jack! Hi, Cy!" He is overjoyed to greet them again just as he did thirty-five years ago, to celebrate the same sportive rites, to yell the same yells, to repeat the same gestures, and to obey the same signals, given by the cheerleader over a megaphone between repeated somersaults.

The Saturday I attended the Harvard-Yale game

was a red-letter day for Cyrus. For the occasion he was sporting a straw boater with a purple hatband and in his buttonhole he had stuck a huge crimson button proclaiming a defiant "To Hell With Yale." Every time the Harvard team made a gain, he would leap to his feet and utter a warcry, while his friend Jack would add a strident note to the revailing uproar by blowing lustily on a trumpet.

Seated quietly beside Cyrus in the middle of 48,000 other hysterical "rooters," I had the strange feeling of being, by sole virtue of my composure, the last guardian of human dignity.

"Now if there's something you don't understand," he told me in almost the same words I had used to him in explaining the niceties of cricket, "just ask me. I'm pretty darn sure I won't be able to explain it."

And yet, good lord! it was at just this moment that we were linked together by the *strongest* of all bonds. For if there's one thing Englishmen and Americans have in common it's their love of sport; it's that undying affection for their old school.

Well, Harvard was winning. In fact, Harvard had won! This was one of the great days in Cyrus Lippcott's life! On the train transporting him from the joys of college back to the adult world, he continued yelling "Go, team, go" between generous slugs of whisky. And I couldn't help wondering if in real life he had ever known moments when he was as blissful as in his college days, moments when he was as free to practice America's true religion—happiness.

For Latins in general, and for the French in particular, the notion of happiness is tainted with relativity. A millennial wisdom, handed down with other hereditary characteristics, teaches them from childhood that happiness is fleeting. "*Good year, lean year*. . . . Where there's an up, there'll be a down! . . . Life is short, so make the most of it! . . . He who laughs on Friday will weep on Sunday!" Such is the forest of melancholy refrains in which the French child grows up.

It's a different story here in America where happiness forms part of the daily program. What am I saying? From the *very* beginning in the charter that launched the American ship of state, happiness was included. The United States is, I suppose, the only country in the world that formally guarantees happiness to its nationals. The Declaration of Independence, carefully preserved under glass at the Library of Congress in Washington, ranks happiness among the inalienable rights of citizenship: life, liberty, and the pursuit of happiness.

The pursuit of happiness! When an American is deprived of his happiness, he feels as unjustly hit as a Frenchman who's been deprived of his hunting license.

That's doubtless why when unhappy *he* consults one of those professors of human happiness who will prescribe a treatment for him with all the precision of a laryngologist.

An American has this notion of guaranteed happiness instilled in him from a tender age. In the Old World a child is treated to a daily diet of admonishments: "Sit up straight!" "Behave yourself!" "Say 'thank you,'" "Shut up!" "Keep quiet!," "Watch that elbow!," "Finish what's on your plate!," "Say 'Good Morning' to the lady!" and between two cuffs on the ears he learns that life is made up of things one shouldn't do. The American child at the same age is stuffed full of ice cream, popcorn, TV shows, vitamins, milk, fruit juice, music, toys, and he grows up in an atmosphere of incredible freedom, where slaps, naughty boy's corners, and dunce's caps are unknown. His is a world where the most frequently heard phrase is: "How nice!" A world where the only constraints are reserved for parents who must refrain from giving their children complexes by forcing them to act against their natures. A world where the young shoot must be allowed to grow up unobstructed.[1]

[1] The Pochets were amazed at the number of left-handed people they encountered in the United States. Many write with their left hand close to their bodies, with the elbow sticking out. This is usually due to the parents' reluctance to break the child of his habit if he begins to write that way.

I learned this to my cost one October evening in Kansas City. I was watching some young ruffians splashing tar over a shop window when I got a cupful right in the mustache—all under the mocking eye of a policeman. I advanced on him, shaking my umbrella with indignation. Whereupon the "cop" said: "Don't you know it's Halloween?" And without paying further heed to the incident, he went on directing traffic with his white-gloved hand.

It was thus I learned, somewhat too late, that Halloween is the children's day of grace, when they can do anything with impunity that they take it into their sweet heads to do.

It is when he gets to college that the American child finally quarries the happiness he has been pursuing from birth. In these dream colleges he spends four years, sheltered from the harsh contingencies of life. Here he "dates" the loveliest girls in the world while taking courses with professors who look as though they had just come from Hollywood. Cicero and fluid drive, logic and rock an' roll, Shakespeare at eleven and Barbara at five, anthropology and baseball, Kant and blue jeans, evenings spent in smoke-filled "dens," days spent sauntering across the grassy expanses of green campuses—all this is really paradise on earth.

I often wonder, therefore, why it is that Lippcott and

his fellow countrymen, the most spoiled ex-children in the world, spend fortunes on psychiatrists and on the purchase of such happiness textbooks as *How to be happily married* or *How to get rid of your worries.*

Emerging first from a world where all is permitted and then from a collegiate paradise where all seems easy, the pampered young American runs headlong into the realities of life and realizes that the happiness promised him by the Declaration of Independence is not always easy of attainment. He cannot, however, complain of not being aided in his quest. Magazines, advertisements, and television dog his every step with a multicolored theory of felicity. His thought is moulded by the syntax of success— that of the media of mass publicity. Life is served up to him on a platter as an uninterrupted series of sunny days; a paradise in which every car has that "million-dollar look," [2] with a gear shift "smooth as cream" propelling him as effortlessly as a cloud"; where all airplanes are *luxurious,* all women *glamorous,* all nightclubs packed with *charm* and *excitement,* all meals *sumptuous;* where all trips are "passports to happiness"—veritable magic car-

wwwwwwwwwwwwww

[2] The Southern Pacific Railroad puts out a folder vaunting the luxury and comfort of its Portland–San Francisco streamliner, which it terms "the million-dollar train with the million-dollar view."

pets bathed in enchanted moonlight—where everything is fabulous, fashionable, rich, comfortable, brilliant, dazzling, lavish, princely, distinguished, exclusive, select, unique, of the period (no matter which), de luxe, and has "real class"; where everything is of a rosy hue, the color of America itself.

At the Lippcotts everything that can stand a touch of rose has been brightened with this color or its variants, everything from crushed strawberry, tea rose, old rose, to toothpaste pink and that *baby pink* which the old ladies like so much. Lippcott's three-tone car has a pink roof; his tie has pink stripes; Mrs. Lippcott's gloves are pink, as are her hats and the linings of her coats. The sofas of their Schenectady house are pink, as are the table napkins and the collar on their dog. Many of the things the Lippcotts like to eat—sherbets, ice creams, cakes—are pink. Even death has a rosy hue, for, as everyone knows, the morticians will see to it that Lippcott looks more rosy-cheeked than ever the day of his death.

Lippcott is the proud citizen of a country where thousands of brains work reverently every day in calculations intended to conserve his energy—to figure out the number of steps needed to move from the sink to the refrigerator, the ideal height for beds so that they can be made up without fatigue, even birdcages constructed so

"How to succeed, 50 *cents*. . . ."

as to allow one to slip in a clean new tray (complete with simulated gravel) to replace the spotted one.

And yet I can't help wondering if good old Lippcott —the proud possessor of a vocabulary of happiness, a constitution of happiness, and the most gigantic assortment of happiness-producing gadgets in the world—is happy; and if he hasn't been running all his life after that happiness which his college made him taste for one brief instant.

For, generally speaking, Lippcott seems worried.

And what does Lippcott worry about?

About everything. About his wife, about his job, about the Stock Market, about the President's health, about death, about his vacation, about war—even about his hydramatic de luxe Cadillac; which might tomorrow be dethroned by an ever more deluxized machine. If the United States is so overrun with experts writing books entitled *How to get rid of your worries,* it's because people have them on the brain.[3] A recent Gallup Poll reported that

[3] One of the latest of these manuals is called *How to Live 365 Days a Year,* by Dr. John A. Schindler. "Do you," asks the author, "want these 365 days to be an uninterrupted series, an exciting sequence of glorious minutes? . . . Do you want to skip joyously, enthusiastically and singing a gay air along the golden road of life?" Of course, you do. . . . Well, the secret is to have "healthy emotions" and first of all to get rid of all excess worries. "Begin today," Dr. Schindler advises, "it's enough for you to say to yourself: from now on I'm going to behave serenely, calmly, joyfully. Well, all your stock of emotions will be renewed."

"I'm very worried about Cyrus: the doctor says the air of the office is the only one that suits him."

nine out of every ten Americans are a prey to preoccupations, anxieties, fears, and even guilt complexes. "Stop worrying! Relax and forget it!" they are exhorted from all sides.

It's an odd thing. . . . There's not a country in the world where people talk more about "sex" or where there is a greater display of "sexy" pictures and sexual theories than the United States. Nor is there a country in the world where people talk more about relaxation, rest cures, and happiness. And yet love and happiness seem more easily attained by a Normandy farmer or a San Gimignano cobbler than by Lippcott, for whom, in fact, happiness is one more worry. Brought up on a religion of work, output, and productivity, he is restless when he has nothing to do. The dismay he felt in Venice the day his guided-tour program indicated "Free morning" is only one symptom of this restlessness. *Farniente* is for him an unknown word.

As soon as there's no longer a button to be pressed, a handle to be turned, a trigger to be fired, a pedal to be pushed, a plan to be executed—in a word, something to do—Lippcott is disoriented. His greatest enemy is not the U.S.S.R.: it's solitude. Basically he would rather be face to face with a Russian than with himself. Radios, cars, television, films, gadgets, magazines are each day mass-produced, steadily perfected, to fill his fear of the void.

There is, of course, all the difference in the world between the desperate Russian who drowns himself in vodka and with a haggard eye turns to Aliovna Ivanovna and asks: "Life, Aliovna Ivanovna, is life worth living?" and the melancholic American who can, when feeling blue, buy a Cadillac or take a trip to Naples—and pay for it later.

But even at the risk of getting myself put down as a subversive by the F.B.I., I must say that there are more points in common between four Russians who retire to a room in the National Hotel in Moscow to drown themselves in vodka and four Americans who decide: "Let's go out and get drunk!" than there are between a Swiss and a Frenchman.

These two peoples love to drink: one of them to forget everything and to pose the big question, the other to stop thinking and to stop asking questions. Both are fond of group distractions, breaking records, and collective efforts. Both are conscious of their individual weaknesses and the crushing power of their collectivities. Both live for the future—even in daily life. (No woman can forget a night of love-making more quickly than an American.)

After all, the welfare of the world may lie in a well-planned marriage of whisky and vodka. And since one must respect that damnable French law of the triangle, let's throw in the *coq au vin* for good measure.

Chapter 20

[P.D.]

WITH POCHET IN A PLANE

Whenever I board an airplane, I always pray to Heaven to give me a neighbor who has never flown before. For this is the only kind of traveler who can't talk of his previous flight experiences. And who smiles . . . a forced smile, sometimes, to give himself courage, but still a smile. I've begun to think, alas, that this species of traveler has vanished from the face of the earth. Usually I get veteran globe-trotters who look with an axious eye at the chain of the Andes which they have flown over twenty times and who give me a detailed description, as we are coming in to land, of how in 1937 they almost cracked up in Karachi trying to make a one-wheel landing.

The return trip from New York to Paris was in this respect worse than anything I had anticipated. The Major was fortunate to find a seat up ahead. But my neighbor was Pochet, and damned if the fellow wasn't an aeronautical enthusiast and expert just because he once piloted a Blériot back in 1934.

The moment we had finished testing the motors at the end of the runway I saw Pochet take out his chronometer and count the seconds.

"*Un . . . deux . . . trois . . . quatre . . .* mighty long getting off the ground," he remarked. "I admit that with these *machines* you have to check a hundred different things before the take-off, but still something must be wrong. We ought to be in the air already."

We soon were, quite normally as far as I could see, and the plane began to gain height as most planes fortunately do. As we went into a slow bank Pochet started to tell me about air pockets and compared our plane's stability to that of another—far superior according to him.

"Besides," he confided to me, "they're soon going to scrap these *vieux taxis. Je le sais.* I have a friend in the company. . . . Another ten trips at most, and all this *matériel* will be discarded."

Shall I be frank? I don't much like getting into a plane that is making its first flight, but I like even less knowing it's on one of its last. Unlike Sonia, who's always on the *qui-vive* ("Eh! don't you think the left engine's catching fire?") I usually try not to notice all those little things on the wings that ooze, trickle, tremble, and seem about to fall off. This time I surprised myself by actually staring at them fixedly. Everything seemed to be holding together all right. We were soaring through space with swanlike ease when, half an hour later, I saw Pochet turn nervously in his seat and look at his watch again.

"I really don't know," he said, "what they're waiting for *pour faire leur changement de régime.*" [1]

I wondered why he didn't get up and go forward to the pilot's cabin to point out this oversight. This *changement* of the *régime* had me worried. One more thing I knew nothing about! How much happier I was before! Why change the *régime* when everything seemed to be going so smoothly? This damned Pochet was getting me all worked up. I imagined the drama up forward in the cockpit: the pilot struggling desperately with the controls . . . the engines refusing to slow down . . . the radio sending out SOS's. I envied the young American couple in front of us who, in the absence of an expert, had unfolded a map

wwwwwwwwwwww

[1] "To change air speed," the change from climbing to cruising speed. (W.M.T.)

of Paris on their knees and were running their fingers across the Place de la Concorde as though they were there already. Ah, happy youth!

Suddenly the engines seemed to stall.

"That's it!" said Pochet.

"What?" I asked him, my throat in a knot.

"Why the *changement de régime!* They certainly took their time!"

I breathed again. For several more hours, I must admit, my tyrant left me in peace. I would have stayed there, no doubt, if during the night we hadn't run into a storm (an exceptionally violent one, like all storms). Now, I like a storm. I like the ocean. I like a plane. But I don't like all three at once. I said as much to Pochet, who had been awakened by the thunder. But experts are like doctors: just get worried, and they reassure you; take things lightly and they get all het up.

"You are in a Faraday cage," Pochet said. "You have nothing to fear."

"I understand," I said, without understanding, "but . . ."

"*Savez-vous,*" interrupted our expert (certain of my ignorance), "that four planes in every hundred get struck by lightning without the passengers ever noticing it?"

I replied that for the moment I would rather get

struck by something else. But already Pochet was telling me about his past storms, compared to which this one was just a *"vulgaire pétard."*

"Over the Sahara, in the middle of a night like this, I saw a ball of fire go right through the plane. What do you say to that?"

I said nothing, naturally.

"It is all quite normal. Besides, as long as you do not see the hostess strolling casually up the aisle among the passengers for no good reason, you can be sure it is nothing serious."

He had hardly uttered these words when the cabin door opened. Like a spectral apparition in the bluish penumbra, the hostess moved slowly toward us as though she were modeling a dress by Fath. I began to look around at the heads of my fellow passengers thinking they would be the last I would see on this earth. They seemed somber enough.

To while away the time still left to me and to think of something else, I picked up one of the attractive folders graciously placed at my disposal in the pouch in front of me. But luck was against me! The very first I looked at was called *How to Ditch without a Hitch.* A charming, reassuring little folder in color which tells you just what steps to follow to land in mid-ocean "with the grace and serenity of a seagull!" Being shipwrecked was made out to be such a picnic that it was positively mouth-watering. The drawings showing the survivors playing cards under a parasol on their life raft struck me as being closer to Watteau's *Embarquement pour l'île de Cythère* than to Gericault's *Radeau de la Méduse*. The text was no less sprightly. "*Your life jacket, of a striking yellow color and handsomely tailored, can be found in a pocket up above your head. In case of ditching, remove all pointed objects to be found in your pockets; loosen your collar; remove your tie; take off your shoes; but don't undress any further.* [I was already beginning to shiver.] *You'll be that much warmer in the life raft. Put on your life jacket, just as you would slip on a sweater, and tie the upper string ends in a butterfly knot.* [There's at least one thing I'd forget to do in all this, another I wouldn't know how to (the butterfly knot), and a third I would do backward. *Inflate your jacket when you are requested to do so. It is very easy. All you have to do is to give a sharp tug on the two lower strings. If the jacket does not inflate immediately* [so it's not that easy!] *turn the end of the rubber tube in a clockwise direction.* [No folder is really instructive unless it mentions clocks somewhere along the line.]"

"For the rest, there's nothing to worry about! *All our planes carry an adequate supply of life rafts, all of them equipped for maximum comfort: radio, fishing tackle, and adjustable parasols. You now know all you need to know about ditching. Relax and enjoy your trip!"*

I gave it a try, but without much luck. Seeing me awake, the charming hostess bent a strangely angelic-looking face down toward me: "Is there anything you need?"

"I've got everything," I said, without adding that I had too much, thinking, despite myself, that if she could remove my neighbor I could die more peacefully.

After the hostess walked away, the captain came out of the cabin, followed by another officer, and then a third. So many people came out of the cabin that I wondered who could ever have stayed behind. The three men walked back to the rear of the plane—as though the engines were in the tail. The simple fact that they had gone back to have a drink at the bar was, however, reassuring.

"They seem pretty young to me!" said Pochet.

Whereupon he painted a portrait of a pilot so perfect that I assumed he was non-existent ("not too young or too old, unmarried but still not too glamorous, full of *sang-froid* but not reckless, above all, a non-drinker, and a non-smoker, too . . . but he must still like life sufficiently").

Meanwhile, to skirt the troubled zone, the plane began to climb in the night. It even seemed to me that we were climbing terribly.

"If this goes on," I said to Pochet, trying to smile, "we're going to end up in another world."

But our expert was no longer in a joking mood. Pencil in hand, he was busy with mysterious calculations. I fell asleep. When I woke up, it was already day. The Major, fully shaved, seemed in excellent spirits.

"Had a bit of a picnic last night, didn't we?" he cried, apparently delighted to have gotten in a good bout with the heavens.

Pochet, however, was still engrossed in his calculations: "In five minutes, Major, unless I have made a mistake, you will see Finistère."

I marveled at his science when the coast came into sight. But at that moment we were handed a sheet of paper which stated: "The city you are about to fly over is Bordeaux."

"They must have changed course without my noticing it," said Pochet.

Somewhat embarrassed, he didn't say another word until we reached Orly, where we landed as we had flown— without a hitch.

Translator's Epilogue

[W . M . T .]

"THE EARTH ISN'T THAT AT ALL!"

The Grand Tour is over. Everyone is satisfied. Martine is delighted to be back again in Paris by Nicholas's side.[1] New York, however, allowed her to *dégoter des tas de petites choses merveilleuses* and to bring back several trunkfuls of those "gadgets" whose sole purpose will be to dazzle her friends. The one exception is a little pocket vacuum-cleaner, which she uses for every conceivable

wwwwwwwwwwwww

[1] A compromise solution was finally found for the problem of the Thompson boys' schooling. It was decided that the elder, Marc, should enter the Major's old school to receive a final lick of "British polish," but Martine got her way with the younger, who is to remain in French hands up to the baccalaureat. (P.D.)

purpose—for removing specks of dust from my suits and even for spring-cleaning my mustache. It never would have occurred to me that an ex-officer of the Indian Army might one day be vacuum-cleaned by his wife, but this isn't the first time French women have surprised me.

Mme Pochet, for her part, seems to have stripped the New York shops of countless articles in nylon, dacron, and orlon which she just couldn't resist. Thus does the world witness a veritable peacetime pillage. For while the Pochets were pillaging the United States, I'll wager that the O'Connors were devastating Tuscany and carrying off all the silk and leather they could lay their hands on.

As for Pochet, he is, as they say in America, "happy as a clam." He has rediscovered France and her *cuisine*. And with the U.S.A. in his pocket, he is way ahead of his friend Taupin, who can wax lyrical only over the beauties of the Estoril. Both the Pochets, in fact, have come back shockingly Americanized, and mongrel expressions like *"Faire du shopping," "le standing de la vie," "Je vais check-uper,"* and *"avaler un snack"* are forever on the tips of their tongues. They are even getting ready to send out Christmas cards to all their friends signed "Les Pochets."

Should I, I wonder, admit that I am a trifle relieved to be back? I am definitely no more made for American life than the Archbishop of Canterbury is for the Folies-

Bergère. It's true that I failed to get Martine to consider a prolonged sojourn in the United Kingdom, but I have no doubt that she will one day come to appreciate its subtle charms.

As for my friend, Daninos, he has, I must say, kept his promise in allowing me to get in a word here and there, and he has been more than generous in letting me round off this book in proper style.

When I think that Daninos had the misfortune the very first day to stumble on an un-English Englishman who insisted on talking of his stomach! How after that can I ever appear to him *digne de foi?* It's always the same story: in countries as rich in individuality as France, England, and the United States, you have only to enunciate some general rule to encounter its exception. In fact, you encounter nothing but exceptions. The average Englishman, the average American, the average Frenchman are abstract creatures from the spectral kingdom of statistics. Pochet was fundamentally right when he kept repeating to me: *"La France, Major, ce n'est pas ça!"* And so am I when I say to Daninos: "England isn't that at all!"

A big country is never *that!* People are always saying: "The English, the French, the Americans . . ." But you have only to meet one to be prevented from putting him in the plural. The more a man resembles others, the more he considers it a point of pride to be considered different. The odd thing, however, is that, no matter how many exceptions travelers may meet, the popular images that peoples have of each other are always composed of preconceived ideas—so irritating to the national victims.

When a country has won a name for itself because of its Camembert, to the point where it means Camembert and nothing else to the neophyte crossing the border, Camembert begins to get under its skin. People exasperate the Swiss by talking their ears off about their watches, the Italians suffer from their *pastas*, the Spaniards their *toros*, and the Australians their kangaroos. And why the devil do the French think they're doing me a favor by always seating me where there's a good draft? Are they themselves overjoyed when a young Yankee, the sparkle in his eye kindled by the *ville lumière*, gives them his definition of France: *"Gay Paree . . . Montmartre . . . la Tour Eiffel . . . les petites femmes . . . oh là là?"*

But there's no use battling against such ideas, each day mown down and each day deeper rooted. The Eiffel Tower, the Folies-Bergère, and the *oh là là* will always outshine the Descartes, the Pasteurs, and all the Richelieus of France.

Tomorrow the Swiss could become the possessors of the richest uranium deposits on the globe, but the world would go on thinking of them as lactic-and-aseptic watch-makers who never leave a scrap of paper lying around. There's nothing like the Coldstream Guard's black busby and scarlet tunic for a British travel poster, and while there isn't one American in a thousand who lives in a sky-scraper, the average Frenchman likes to imagine Joe Doakes shaving (electrically) on the fifty-eighth floor of the Empire State Building. Now and again an enterprising globe-trotter will deliver a lecture explaining that Amer-icans have a predilection for one-story houses, never do more than 50 mph on the turnpikes, and travel in rather slow-moving trains—but the next day it will all have gone with the wind. A good Hollywood thriller is enough to sweep away the pedestrian truth and, with the aid of cars screaming through red lights and racing trains whose wailing sirens pierce the night, it can quickly revive that postcard picture of America—the one everybody wants.

No, the entire earth is not that at all!

The more I travel, the more lost I become, and the less sure I am of really knowing mankind. Perhaps dis-covery has three phases: a period of preconceived ideas, followed by the collapse of these fairy-tale realms, and finally, much later, the return to certain ideas that, basic-ally, were not altogether false. . . . From the imaginary

"*And there's our house; from that second-story window you can see the White House on a clear day.*"

to the real, and from the real to the imaginary is all that is needed on this confounded planet to throw the most sure-footed explorer off his stride.

Does our planet even possess a center of gravity? I have wondered about it for many years, but I now think I have discovered it at last. Yes, after a long quest, I have found the center of the earth. To tell the truth, I had intended keeping this "top" secret to myself. But the moment has come to reveal it, just as before I was moved to reveal the secret of the American female.

No, my dear Pochet, the hub of the universe is not England, happy as you would be to hear me claim it. Besides, everyone knows that England needs no introduction to the solar system.

The middle of the planet, the center of gravity of the world, is not, as one might think, situated somewhere along the equator, in the bowels of the earth.

It is not New York, or Paris either.

The center of the world is Zanzibar, Rejkjavik, Sydney, or Istanbul. The center of the world is wherever you happen to be. For there you will certainly be able to find planisphere maps. And a planisphere map-maker always arranges to set his own country in the very center of the chart. The docile universe must bow.

One day behind the head of an important Swiss official in Berne I perceived that Switzerland was located in the very center of the globe.

"Look," he said to me, "equidistant from Chicago and Peking, the North Pole and Dakar, our country is really and truly the center of the world."

My haphazard peregrinations having subsequently taken me to Bolivia, I noticed that the center of the world had displaced itself with me. On the immense wall-map serving to tapestry the Bolivian minister's office, Sucre had become the heart of the planet.

"Look," he said to me, "equidistant from Paris and Vancouver, Sydney and Moscow, Bolivia occupies a unique position in the world."

I looked. And, for a moment, I had the impression that the universe was revolving around Sucre.

From Sucre, radiating out toward every azimuth, went arrows that seemed to diffuse over the world their beneficent powers. Tucked away up in the right-hand corner, at the tip of a tiny peninsula, France was accorded approximately the same place that the school children of Limoges usually give Kamchatka or the Aleutians.

Back in Paris I sought to reassure myself by opening Nicholas's atlas to see just where France was.

Well, I found France again, a solid mauve block plumb in the center of the double-page spread in the middle of the book. Paris at high noon, on meridian zero, equidistant from New York and Bombay, Greenland and Ethiopia, marvelously situated, like Sucre and Zanzibar, exactly in the center of the globe!

And so it is that the geographic sense is inculcated in the sweet heads of little Frenchmen, little Danes, and little Zanzibarians.

A NOTE ON THE
AUTHOR

PIERRE DANINOS *was born in 1913 in Paris. After working for various newspapers and serving in the French Army in World War II as a liaison agent, he wrote numerous books of humor. In 1954 his delightful impersonation of a British major first appeared in the pages of* Figaro, *and by now the number of friends that W. Marmaduke Thompson has made at home and abroad with his* Notebooks, *translated in ten countries, is inestimable. Pierre Daninos has visited America three times, and in 1955 traveled the States from coast to coast. He lives in Neuilly-sur-Seine with his wife and three children.*

A NOTE ON THE

T Y P E

IN WHICH THIS BOOK IS SET

THE TEXT *of this book is set in* Caledonia, *a Linotype face designed by* W. A. DWIGGINS *(1880-1956), who was responsible for so much that is good in contemporary book design. Though much of his early work was in advertising and he was the author of the standard volume* Layout in Advertising. *Mr. Dwiggins later devoted his prolific talents to book typography and type design, and worked with great distinction in both fields. In addition to his designs for Caledonia, he created the Metro, Electra, and Eldorado series of type faces, as well as a number of experimental cuttings that have never been issued commercially.*

Caledonia belongs to the family of printing types called "modern face" by printers—a term used to mark the change in style of typeletters that occurred at the end of the eighteenth century. It is best evidenced in the letter shapes designed by Baskerville, Martin, Bodoni, and the Didots.

This book was composed, printed, and bound by H. WOLFF, *New York. The paper was made by* S. D. WARREN CO., *Boston.*